A MATHEMATICIAN EXPLAINS

THE UNIVERSITY OF CHICAGO PRESS, CHICAGO

THE BAKER & TAYLOR COMPANY, NEW YORK; THE CAMBRIDGE UNIVERSITY
PRESS, LONDON; THE MARUZEN-KABUSHIKI-KAISHA, TOKYO, OSAKA,
KYOTO, FUKUOKA, SENDAI; THE COMMERCIAL PRESS, LIMITED, SHANGHAI

A MATHEMATICIAN EXPLAINS

BY

MAYME I. LOGSDON

ASSOCIATE PROFESSOR OF MATHEMATICS

THE UNIVERSITY OF CHICAGO

DECORATIVE DRAWINGS BY

CHICHI LASLEY

THE UNIVERSITY OF CHICAGO PRESS

CHICAGO · ILLINOIS

PREFACE

THE idea that each individual has something to gain by acquiring a knowledge of mathematics is not new. According to Plato,* "the art of calculation (*logistika*) and arithmetic are both concerned with number; those who have a natural gift for calculating have, generally speaking, a talent for learning of all kinds, and even those who are slow are, by practice in it, made smarter. But the art of calculation is only preparatory to the true science; those who are to govern the city are to get a grasp of *logistika*, not in the popular sense with a view to use in trade, but only for the purpose of knowledge, until they are able to contemplate the nature of number in itself by thought alone."

The college curriculum of the University of Chicago, adopted in 1930, includes a course of three lectures per week for one year in the physical sciences, paralleled with small-group discussions. The conduct and content of this course, which is required of all college students, are motivated by the knowledge that many persons pass through youth, adulthood, and old age with no understanding of, or interest in, the operation of natural laws.

This course, planned for the student who has no native interest in the physical sciences, is perforce entirely different from a course which might be designed for a student who has a definite interest in this field. Its aim is to provide explanations for what is happening about us and to show with some detail how the human race through the ages has arrived

*Adapted from Plato, *The Republic*, pp. 525–26.

at the explanations here presented. In this development mathematics plays a twofold rôle, viz., the unfolding and attaining of pure mathematical theory and the invention of mathematical processes as aids to astronomy, physics, geology, and chemistry. In ancient times the latter was the predominating function of the science called "exact"; in modern times the former aspect of mathematics has become of ever increasing importance.

The attempt to give in a few lectures a vivid picture of the historical development of the mathematics of classical times with a description of the types of problems which led to the growth of elementary concepts of arithmetic, algebra, geometry, and trigonometry, and to give something of the purport and processes of the modern subjects, analytical geometry and the calculus, to the end that the student may obtain fairly definite ideas of their meanings and uses in modern life and of their relations to the various fields of the physical sciences, has been rendered more difficult than pleasant by the lack of satisfactory references for extensive reading; and it is to meet that need that this book has been written. In it the subjects which may be considered important for the general education of a person who is not a specialist in a physical science have a more complete treatment than can be given in a few lectures, but at the same time the text does not go so far afield as to confuse with new ideas or with technical notions. It does not take the place of any one or more texts in the standard courses in college mathematics, but its sponsors believe that it will prove to be of use along the following lines:

(1) To provide the mathematics for general physical science courses, as at the University of Chicago.

(2) To serve as a text for a one-hour or a two-hour orientation course in college, junior college, or senior high school.

(3) To serve as a reading reference for first-year and second-year mathematical courses in college or junior college.

(4) To serve as a supplementary text for courses in the teaching of mathematics in normal schools and teachers colleges.

(5) To serve as an eye-opener for the adult who knows no mathematics beyond elementary algebra and geometry but who has a healthy curiosity concerning the science whose development has made possible this age of the machine.

Acknowledgments are due and are gratefully rendered to Professor Gilbert A. Bliss, who contributed chapter 8, "Mathematical Interpretations of Geometrical and Physical Phenomena" (two lectures in the general course mentioned above); to the editors of the American Mathematical Monthly, for permission to reprint it (with minor changes) from Vol. 40 (1933); to Mrs. Ardis Monk, who read the manuscript and whose experience as a discussion group leader enabled her to offer valuable suggestions as to emphasis and method of presentation; to Mr. Carl Denbow, Fellow in mathematics at the University of Chicago, whose constructive criticism of the manuscript resulted in the smoothing-out of many rough places; to Mr. A. Boyd Newborn of the University of Arizona for aid in preparing copy for the cuts; to Mrs. Chichi Lasley, the artist who provided the illustrations; and to Mr. Donald Bean and his able assistants who saw the book through the press.

MAYME I. LOGSDON

THE UNIVERSITY OF CHICAGO
October 3, 1935

TABLE OF CONTENTS

CHRONOLOGICAL
LIST OF MATHEMATICIANS

AHMES (18th or 19th century B.C.)
THALES (640–550 B.C.)
PYTHAGORAS (569–500 B.C.)
EUCLID (300 B.C.)
ERATOSTHENES (276–194 B.C.)
ARISTARCHUS (310–? B.C.)
APOLLONIUS (250–200 B.C.)
HIPPARCHUS (180–125 B.C.)
DIOPHANTUS, *Arithmetica* (275 A.D.)
HYPATIA (375–415 A.D.)

ARYABHATTA (476–550 A.D.)
MAHAVIR, *Arithmetic* (c. 925 A.D.)
BHASKARA (b. 1114 A.D.)
TARTAGLIA (1500–1557)
CARDAN (1501–1576)
GALILEO (1564–1642)
DESCARTES (1596–1650)
NEWTON (1642–1727)
LEIBNIZ (1646–1716)
ABEL (1802–1829)

CHAPTER 1

NATURE OF MATHEMATICS

A PUPIL of Euclid, when he had learned a proposition, inquired: "What advantage shall I get by learning these things?" Euclid called a slave and said, "Give him a sixpence, since he must needs gain by what he learns."

It is not the purpose of this book to attempt to give to the reader a knowledge and skill in the use of mathematics which will make of him a better money-gatherer, but rather to come to the aid of the many who reach adult years with a distaste for mathematics and a pronounced inferiority complex with regard to it, and who at the same time suffer an occasional feeling of embarrassment at their inability to understand some apparently simple natural or mechanical law. Most of these persons have more or less curiosity concerning the science of which they know little and would gladly undertake to acquire an understanding of the origins and uses of mathematics if they were convinced that this could be done in an informal way without the necessity of drawing on a supposed-known-but-long-since-forgotten secondary-school mathematical training.

Elementary mathematics includes arithmetic, algebra, geometry, trigonometry, analytical geometry, and the calculus. We shall try to trace some of the important steps in the development of these subjects from their beginnings, showing that an advance in the growth of the science was the direct or indirect attempt to *satisfy a definite human need*.

A second objective is to show something of the importance of mathematics and the mathematical sciences in *enriching the intellectual life* of the twentieth century, as well as in contributing to the *physical comfort* and the *recreational pleasures*.

A third objective is to look carefully into the *nature of the science* which is commonly labeled "abstract" and "deductive," and show that these descriptive terms need not imply that behind them lie mystery and difficulty of comprehension, but rather beauty, elegance, and, above all, *orderliness* and *simplicity*.

The history of mathematics dates back to the beginning of civilization, and there is a remarkable parallelism between the various stages of its development and the mathematical experiences of each reader of these pages through his childhood, his youth, and his adult years. By constantly keeping this parallelism in evidence, by giving numerous specific examples and outlining their methods of attack, by keeping the language as non-technical as is consistent with accuracy and clear thinking, and by showing many connections of mathematics with everyday life, the author hopes to give to the general reader a picture of what mathematics is, what it does, and (a very little of) how it does it.

Indeed, a little attention leads to the feeling that this science, though rightly called "abstract," is, in reality, deeply human and alive and that it is not impossible to inform one's self concerning the why's and how's without actually acquiring the technique of the doing; for, let it be definitely understood that this book is a book of information, not a teaching book. In the presentation of scientific facts, however, it is inevitable that enough of method must be given to enable the reader to follow a succession of steps to a logical conclusion. Hence it is hoped that an important by-product of the reading of this book will be the intellectual appreciation of the power and the elegance of deductive reasoning.

1. Mathematics an abstract science. It is certain that primitive man, of whatever race, had a manner of designating two sheep, three horses, ten warriors, long before he had a concept of, and words or symbols for, the abstract numbers 2, 3, 10. The small child has an understanding of what is meant by two apples, two chairs, five marbles, before he is able to abstract the numeral from its noun. Early problems in the kindergarten and elementary grades are concrete:

> Tom has 10 cents and spends 2 cents for a pencil. How many cents has he left?
> John has three apples and his brother has three apples. How many apples do the two boys have?
> How much will five books cost at 50 cents each?

A little thought convinces that the intellectual processes involved in solving these "story" problems are simpler in the beginning than those needed for the comprehension and solution of

$$10-2 = ? \qquad 3+3 = ? \qquad 5 \times 50 = ?$$

When we contemplate the nature of mathematics, we are struck by very significant facts. For example, $3+4 = 7$ may be thought of as relating to dollars or leaves or stars or what you will, but the sentence $3+4 = 7$ is the statement of a mathematical fact which is not necessarily thought of as associated with any physical object or even idea. Indeed, as the study of arithmetic progresses, there seems to be a definite and conscious effort to detach the arithmetical operations from human experiences. The relative number of concrete problems, as compared with the number of abstract computational problems, decreases. It is not surprising that many young people early acquire the pronounced feeling that there is no especial human significance in the science of mathematics.

Let us see if, by looking at particular instances, we can comprehend the reason for the apparent divorcing of mathematics from human experience. We all know more or less precisely what the Law of Gravitation is. We understand that this law explains many phenomena of our everyday life. For example, an apple falls to the earth, the moon does not fall to the earth but revolves around the earth, water runs down hill, a ball when thrown into the air falls back to the earth, the moon produces tides on the earth's surface—these are facts of observation explained by the Law of Gravitation. But the mathematical explanation of these phenomena makes no mention of the apple, ball, moon, etc. It may be written

$$f = k \frac{mM}{d^2} , \qquad\qquad (1)$$

where m and M are the masses of two bodies, d is the distance between them,* and k is a constant depending on the units of measure, of mass, and of distance. The force f gives the magnitude of the attraction exerted by each body upon the other. Its direction is along the line which joins their centers of gravity.

In equation (1) we have a statement which, assuming an understanding of the laws of motion, not only explains the motion of the apple, the ball, and the other objects mentioned above and of all other earthly objects which have moved, are moving, or will in the future move subject only to the attraction of gravitation, but which also explains the motions of the planets around the sun, of the stars in their courses, of bodies in this universe or in any hypothetical universe in which are being considered the motions of bodies which are subject to no force other than that of the attraction of gravitation.

Newton could never have obtained his Law of Gravitation if he had not noted *that which is common* to a great number of apparently unrelated natural phenomena; and his statement of this law, in which, by ignoring specific examples, he appears to remove it from the realm of everyday experience, actually leaves it free for an unlimited scope of application. *Only by an abstract statement can the field of application be completely unrestricted.*

It is neither possible nor desirable here to attempt to show how the foregoing formula (it is called the *Law of Inverse Squares*) solves all of the problems mentioned, but in the next paragraphs we shall look more closely at the problem of the falling apple. The apple falls to the ground because of the attraction of the earth for it. As long as the stem is green and strong, it can resist the pull of the earth on the apple, although that pull is by no means a slight pull; but when the apple is ripe, the stem becomes more brittle and there comes a time when the pull of the earth (the attraction of gravitation) is strong enough to break the stem, and the apple falls. It is inevitable that there should be motion when a force is acting unless the force is neutralized by a second force. The magnitude of the force, as we learn from equation (1), depends on the mass of the earth, the mass of the apple, and the distance between them; the amount of motion depends on the magnitude of the force.

* By "distance between them" is meant distance between their centers of gravity.

Experiments are frequently performed in physics laboratories to demonstrate the action of bodies free to move when acted upon by an exterior force. Before the time of GALILEO (1564–1642) neither the mathematicians nor the philosophers could agree on whether distances traversed by objects which were subjected to the same force depend on the action of the force alone or on the time during which the force is acting, or on both, or whether the masses of the objects are also effective in determining distances. This is not surprising; in fact, this question could not be answered with precision until Galileo demonstrated that the size and mass of an object falling freely or sliding (with negligible friction) down an inclined plane have no effect on its velocity. Further experiments then and later show that

a) The distance traversed the second second is three times that of the first second,
b) The distance traversed the third second is five times that of the first second,
c) The distance traversed the fourth second is seven times that of the first second,
d) The distance traversed the fifth second is nine times that of the first second, etc.

It is merely repeating the information above, but from a slightly different point of view, if we say:

a) The distance traversed during the first 2 sec. is four times that of the first second,
b) The distance traversed during the first 3 sec. is nine times that of the first second,
c) The distance traversed during the first 4 sec. is sixteen times that of the first second,
d) The distance traversed the first 5 sec. is twenty-five times that of the first second, etc.

Now, a mathematician examines four statements like the last four and seeks for something common in them which he can express in a formula—a formula which not only tells all that has been told in the four statements but also tells what is concealed in the "etc." Without a formula a reader would conclude that the experiments have been carried out and data obtained for a longer interval than 5 sec. but that it is not necessary to take up more space in writing it out, since further items are exactly what one would expect them to be in the light of what has been displayed.

In order to tell all of this and more in a formula, obviously a number symbol must be used to designate the number of seconds, a second symbol is needed to denote the distance traversed during the first second, and a third for the total distance from the beginning. Let us use t for the number of seconds, d for the distance during the first second, and s for the total distance. Let us then write the formula,

$$s = dt^2 \text{ ,}$$

and examine it to see if it gives all of the information which we expect of it. First, put $t = 1$ and you see that $s = d$; put $t = 2$ and compute $s = 4d$; put $t = 3$ and get $s = 9d$; it really is not necessary to go further except to say that, if the data are correct and if we are really justified in believing that the distance continues to behave even for large values of t as it behaves for t not greater than 5, we can use the formula to compute the distance traversed in the first 10 sec., in the first 30 sec., in any chosen number of seconds without writing down the intermediate distances for 6, 7, 8, 9, etc., sec., as would be necessary if we worked only from the information in the form in which it was first given.

As a matter of fact, experience has shown that the formula

$$s = dt^2$$

is correct for an object moving without friction near the surface of the earth when there is no changing force acting on it except the attraction of the earth. Hence, if we know the distance which a given object has moved during the first second, its distance for any desired number of seconds can be computed.

Now let us look into the possible values of d. Again we go to the laboratory and devise the following experiment: A number of wires are set

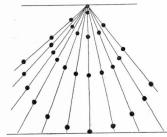

up as in the drawing with varying slants or slopes. On each wire is a bead, and at the beginning of the experiment the beads are equally distant from the floor. They are automatically released at a given instant, and pictures are taken with a motion-picture camera until the first bead reaches the floor. The pictures show that the greatest actual distance (along its wire), as well as the greatest vertical distance, is traversed by the bead on the vertical wire, and that, as the deviation of the wire from the vertical increases, both the actual distance s and the vertical distance decrease. The distance for each bead can be measured, and from these measurements can be determined the effect on the motion which is caused by a given deviation from the vertical.

The distance which the bead on the vertical wire traverses during the first second is, as Galileo's experiment showed, equal to the distance through which any other freely falling body falls during the first second (when it falls from rest). This distance has been measured with great care many times and found to be approximately 16.1 ft. This is a number which occurs repeatedly in problems of motion, and for convenience is usually denoted by $\frac{1}{2}g$.* Its double, g, whose value is 32.2, is called the **acceleration of gravity,** for reasons which will appear later. Hence the distance traversed by the vertical bead for any value of t can be computed from the equation

$$s = \tfrac{1}{2}gt^2 \ ,$$

while for the beads on the slanting wires $s = dt^2$. The value of the symbol d is never as large as $\frac{1}{2}g$ and diminishes† as the deviation from the vertical increases.

The equations not only suffice for computing the distance when the time is known but may be used to compute the time when the distance is known. We then write, for the freely falling body,

$$\tfrac{1}{2}gt^2 = s \ , \qquad gt^2 = 2s \ , \qquad t^2 = 2s/g \ , \qquad t = \sqrt{2s/g} \ .$$

For example, you could fall a mile in less than $\frac{1}{2}$ min.—in fact, in less than 26 sec. This seems surprising, since the fall is only 16.1 ft. the first second. Again, we can find the distance an object would fall the twentieth second by subtracting the total distance the first 19 sec., $\frac{1}{2}g(19)^2$ from the total distance the first 20 sec., $\frac{1}{2}g(20)^2$. This gives approximately 624 ft.

In a similar manner the mathematician is able to start with the Law of Inverse Squares and describe the motion of the earth around the sun, the motion of the moon around the earth, the tidal effect of the moon on

---

* Just as π is used for the ratio of the circumference of a circle to its diameter.

† A bead on a slanting wire is subject to two forces, viz., the force of gravity which pulls down and the push of the wire against the bead. The wire pushes in the direction perpendicular to it. The effective force which produces the motion is the resultant of the two forces (see chap. 4, sec. 7).

the earth, etc. He can show you how much higher you could jump if you were on the moon than you can jump on the earth, and can prove to you that if you were on one of the little moons of Mars you could jump high enough to keep on going.

Man jumps from small moon
of Mars

The preceding discussion of the motion of an object which is acted upon by the force of gravity may seem to have led us far from the subject of this section, "The Abstract Nature of Mathematics"; but, indeed, we are still on the subject. The object of these remarks is to emphasize the fact already mentioned, viz., when the mathematician observes that a number of phenomena have a common property, he tries to find a symbolic expression for this common property which expresses the property itself apart from any of the specific objects to which it is attached. He then studies the formula as a purely mathematical product; he is interested in the relation of the symbols which appear in it. He asks himself many questions concerning the mathematical (not the physical) implications of the relationship. When he has a complete understanding of his algebraic relations, he is able to make the objective applications to any of the phenomena to which its origin was due; and moreover, he is quite likely to discover that he is now able to explain, in whole or in part, other phenomena not hitherto thought of as having anything in common with the first group considered.

A second possible result of such a study of a formula or a set of formulas as mathematical entities apart from any physical or geometrical significance must not be overlooked. Not infrequently the development of a purely mathematical theory leads on and on until mathematical situations are developed which have no apparent physical or geometrical explanation. It may or it may not happen that within a decade or a lifetime or a century this theory will be found to be of use in interpreting life about us. An instance of such a situation which is of considerable importance is the development of Einstein's theory of relativity. After plane and solid geometry had been developed, certain geometers went further and developed in detail the geometry in a space of four dimensions and even in a space whose dimension was designated by n, where n was supposed to be an arbitrary positive integer. Now this geometry, when developed analytically (i.e., by means of algebraic formulas), without regard to a visual or imaginative concept as to the makeup of a physical space of four or more dimensions, offers no particular difficulties, and it was this phase of it which interested the mathematician, though the non-mathematician was considerably agitated by the fact that he could not visualize a space of four dimensions and consequently he was certain that no such space exists and that there is something very peculiar about mathematicians who use their time developing theories about it.

Einstein's theory uses the mathematical set-up which is called "the geometry of a space of four dimensions," and it is quite reasonable to believe that the study of the physical concepts involved in this theory could not possibly have preceded the development of the mathematical theory. Einstein, as well as Euclid and Newton, found the way prepared before him.

2. Deductive reasoning. To reason is to draw inferences or conclusions from propositions (statements). The propositions on which the inferences are based may be the result of observations or they may be products of the mind. In the former case, the reasoning is generally called **inductive**; in the latter case, it is called **deductive.**

An excellent *example of inductive reasoning* is the already-mentioned Law of Gravitation of Newton. From his observations, whether in the open or in the laboratory, he concluded that there is always an attraction between two objects, that the attraction results in motion if the objects are free to move, that the attraction depends directly on the masses of the two objects and inversely on the square of their distance apart, and that motion takes place in the line joining the two centers of gravity. An induction always adds something to the observations. Newton's observations could not furnish him with such a precise statement as the inverse square law. That was his own contribution, his guess. How fortunate for him and for us that it turned out to be a satisfactory guess, because, of all hypothetical laws of attraction which have been studied by the mathematician, none is so simple and so easy to understand as the inverse square law.

When an induction, based on observations, is made, it is not intended that it shall be accepted as a universal truth, but it is advanced as a *hypothesis for further study*. Additional observations are then made and the results compared with the results expected from the hypothesis. If there is more deviation between the experimental results and the computed results than can be expected from the inaccuracies of observation and measurement, the scientist discards the hypothesis and tries to formulate another. The Law of Gravitation has been verified for so many cases that it is accepted now as a true statement of the attraction of any two objects in our universe.

"Deductive reasoning" was defined above as drawing inferences or conclusions from propositions or statements which are *products of the mind*. Such propositions (in mathematics they are called **axioms** or **postulates**) are set down arbitrarily as assumptions on which the reasoning is to be based. They may be compared to rules of a game which have been devised and which all players are required to observe. Whether the postulates describe any physical or geometrical situation within the realm of experience has nothing whatever to do with the reasoning; if the conclusions based on the postulates and definitions are in accord with them, the reasoning is **logical**. The following is an example of deductive reasoning: We start with a main proposition or **major premise**, which in this particular instance is a definition, viz., *Two lines in a plane which never meet are said to be parallel*. This is followed by a **minor premise**, which may be an assumption, e.g., *Let the lines* a *and* c *be parallel and also let the lines* b *and* c *be parallel*. The deductive reasoning consists in comparing the two statements and drawing a conclusion therefrom. If the conclusion leads to no absurdity which invalidates one or both of the premises (or the original axioms or any proposition which has been previously proved), the reasoning is logical and the conclusion is a logical conclusion. In the example a logical conclusion is: *Two lines, each of which is parallel to a third line, are parallel to each other; in particular,* a *and* b *are parallel*.

We repeat the statements made above. It is not necessary that the major premise be a definition or even a statement of fact. It may be a pure invention of the mind, of such a nature that no one can find a case in real life which exemplifies it. Where the major premise comes from, or what it means, has nothing whatever to do with the correctness of the conclusion. This must be a conclusion which makes sense (i.e., is logical) in view of the premises.

In everyday life, each individual is constantly making decisions. He is confronted with a certain situation. He must compare propositions and draw an inference. That it is of utmost importance that one be able to reason logically, both inductively and deductively, cannot be denied.

In the very elementary parts mathematics is largely inductive, but in the later stages of the fields discussed in these pages and in the higher mathematics it tends more and more toward the deductive type. In no other part of his school experience does a student receive as much training in deductive thinking as in the study of mathematics. This alone justifies the subject as a part of a school curriculum, but it is hoped that the following pages will show that *mathematics is important to you and to me for its content as well as for its method*.

CHAPTER 2

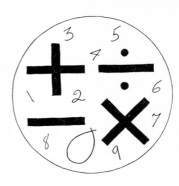

ARITHMETIC

ARITHMETIC is the science of numbers; or, as a mathematician would say, it is the *science of manipulating or operating with numbers*. This sounds more formidable than it really is, as we see when we note that the operations of elementary arithmetic are *addition, subtraction, multiplication, division, raising to a power*, and *extracting a root*.

A set of characters or symbols which are used for numbers and the use of these symbols in counting, adding, etc., is a **number system**. In the development of arithmetic each primitive tribe developed its own number system just as it developed its own word system or language. Some of these number systems were more highly developed than others. They contained more symbols for numbers or a more simple usage of their symbols than other number systems, traces of which have been found. In certain number systems problems of a more complicated nature could be solved than in others, just as in certain early languages larger and richer vocabularies enabled the members of the tribes to give more precise expression to their ideas than in other languages lacking in descriptive terms.

A close examination of the properties of our own number system will be made in the next sections. This will provide a basis for comparison with others and a better understanding of the earlier number systems to be examined later. We wish to understand, on the one hand, why the ancients considered numbers to be mystical entities; on the other hand, we wish to justify the abstract point of view toward his number symbols taken by the modern mathematician.

1. Zero. The principle of position. Our number system uses ten sym-bols—1, 2, 3, 4, 5, 6, 7, 8, 9, and 0—and it has a very important property called the **principle of position** or **position-value.** For example, in the num-bers 4, 41, 472, and 0.04 the symbol 4 at one time stands for the number four, at others it stands for four times ten, four times ten squared, and four times one-tenth squared, respectively,

$$4 \times 10 , \qquad 4 \times 10^2 , \qquad 4 \times (\tfrac{1}{10})^2 .$$

It is obvious that the principle of position is a highly sophisticated notion, and we shall not expect to find the number systems of the ancients endowed with this property. Its importance is apparent, for without it new symbols would be needed for the powers of 10, as in this example.

Of even greater importance than the principle of position in our number system is the fact that we have a **symbol for zero** for which there are two distinct uses. One use of zero denotes *the absence of number*, as, $8 - 8 = 0$, and was so used by a few of the early peoples. In the greater number of cases, however, no traces of such a symbol have been found. As a consequence, a problem whose answer is zero could not be solved in num-ber symbols but would have to be stated in words, or else classified among the problems having no solution.

This is not a state of affairs to occasion surprise, for we certainly do not expect to find that the arithmetic of primitive tribes was sufficiently developed to handle all of the problems for which our arithmetic supplies solutions. For example, a pupil in one of our primary grades would say that there is no solution for the problems: (*a*) "Subtract 8 from 5," and (*b*) "Divide 11 by 5." At that age his arithmetic is an arithmetic of posi-tive integers; and in a number system containing only positive integers, problems (*a*) and (*b*) cannot be solved.

Our notation is called *Arabic* or *Hindu-Arabic;* but it really originated with the Hindus and was borrowed by the Arabs, who introduced it into Spain at the time of the Moorish conquest in the eighth century. We do not know who invented this symbolism or the time of its invention. The nine symbols were supposed to have been in use before zero and the prin-ciple of position were invented. This view receives support* from the

* F. Cajori, *A History of Mathematics* (New York: Macmillan Co., 1909), p. 88.

fact that on the island of Ceylon a notation resembling the Hindu but without the zero has been preserved. We know that Buddhism and Indian culture were transplanted to Ceylon about the third century after Christ,

Aryabhatta putting in zero

and that this culture remained stationary there, while it made progress on the Continent. It seems highly probable, then, that the numerals of Ceylon are the old imperfect numerals of India. In Ceylon nine figures were used for the nine units, nine others for the tens, one for 100, and also one for 1,000. These twenty characters enabled them to write all of the numbers up to 9,999. Thus 8,725 would have been written with six signs representing the following numbers: 8, 1,000, 7, 100, 20, 5. It appears that zero and the accompanying principle of position were introduced into the Hindu number system about the time of ARYABHATTA, an Indian astronomer and mathematician who was born A.D. 476.

Our second use for the zero symbol is explained as follows: In the number 41, for example, the digit 1 is used to *push* the digit 4 into the ten's place; and, indeed, by use of the nine digits in turn as pushers the numbers 41, 42, 43, 44, 45, 46, 47, 48, and 49 can be written. But without a zero, what could be done with such numbers as 470, 401, 4.0003, etc.?

With these two sophisticated concepts of position-value and zero, the compactness and convenience of our number system have enabled modern peoples to develop an arithmetic which has progressed far beyond the elementary arithmetic of the ancients. The subjects of annuities, averages, insurance, mensuration, and partnership give rise to branches, or special applications of arithmetic. More than fifteen thousand research papers in the theory of numbers* have been written. In them are exhibited fascinating properties of numbers.

Handicapped as the ancients were with their multitude of awkward symbols and, generally, the absence of a zero, it is surprising to learn how

* See L. E. Dickson, *History of the Theory of Numbers* (3 vols.; Carnegie Institution of Washington, 1919–23).

much they were able to accomplish. This is only another instance of what man can accomplish under stress. The problems arose, the solutions were desired or needed, and they solved them. However, only the scribes and the priests and a very few scholars had access to the lore of the day.

2. Base of a number system. Commercial transactions between individuals and between different peoples necessitated the development of an arithmetic. Some one has said that the Phoenicians were the first and cleverest traders of the universe: arithmetic is nowhere more useful or more necessary than in commerce; hence the Phoenicians would have to be expert arithmeticians. The collection of rents and taxes, the purchase of land, grain, horses, the payment of laborers, etc.—simple transactions among primitive tribes—required a knowledge of addition and subtraction, if not extensively of multiplication and division. When a civilization reaches a stage where records are to be kept, number symbols must be at hand. Let us see how far some of the ancient tribes progressed in finding a symbolism adequate for their needs.

Our evidence* is found on bits of stone, on mural paintings, on mummy wrappings, clay tablets, pieces of metal, pottery, on papyri, on the pyramids. Number records of a few primitive tribes point to the conclusion that their number concepts did not extend beyond the number 5 and that they had no number symbols other than marks. In general, however, we find that the notation symbols were grouped into *cycles*, depending on the base of the system. It would be natural to count to a certain number and then repeat. With rare exceptions this number is 10. This fact gave rise to the following question formulated by Aristotle (384–322 B.C.) in his *Book of Problems*. He asks, "Why do all peoples, barbarians as well as Greeks, count by tens and not otherwise?" To his own question the greatest philosopher responds that this depends on the

Man counts
ten fingers

fact that the hands of man, natural auxiliary in arithmetical calculations, have in all ten fingers. For this reason, for example, the symbols of

* PHOENIX, son of Agenor, wrote the first arithmetic. It was written in the Phoenician language, but this was many years after the beginnings which are here being discussed.

our system, called a **decimal system** because its base is 10, fall into the cycles

1 ,	2 ,	3 ,	. . . . ,	9 ;
10 ,	20 ,	30 ,	. . . . ,	90 ;
100 ,	200 ,	300 ,	. . . . ,	900 ;
etc.				

The Roman numerals, also a decimal system, but lacking a principle of position,* fall into the cycles

I,	II,	III,	IV,	V,	VI,	VII,	VIII,	IX;
X,	XX,	XXX,	XL,	L,	LX,	LXX,	LXXX,	XC;
C,	CC,	CCC,	CD,	D,	DC,	DCC,	DCCC,	CM;
etc.								

If the system were **ternary,** i.e., with the number 3 as base, the cycles would contain symbols for the following numbers:

1,	2;
3,	6;
9,	18;
27,	54;
etc.	

The symbols employed would resemble, in the manner of combination but not necessarily in appearance, those of the Roman numerals in case the ternary system had no position value. This means that there must be separate symbols for the powers of 3 in the first column, while their doubles in the second column might be represented by repetition, as above. If, however, the system has the principle of position, only three symbols are needed, symbols for 0, 1, and 2. Let us use the Hindu symbols for these numbers when writing numbers in a ternary system and see how it is done.

* While lacking a principle of position in the sense explained above, viz., that of associating with each position a different power of 10, the Roman system has a certain principle of position. For example, in the numbers XI and IX the position of the I in the one case indicates addition; in the other it indicates subtraction. The rule is this: numbers represented by symbols written in juxtaposition are to be added (the **additive principle**) if there is no symbol representing a smaller number than the one on its right. In the latter case, the smaller number is to be subtracted from the one represented by the symbol on its right. This is the **subtractive principle.** Examples are CX, CXX, CL, XC, MDIV, the first three of which exemplify the additive principle only, the fourth showing the subtractive principle only, while in the last example both principles are used.

3. Representation of numbers to other bases than 10. To count from 1 to 20 in the ternary system we write as follows:

1, 2, 10, 11, 12, 20, 21, 22, 100, 101, 102, 110, 111, 112, 120, 121, 122, 200, 201, 202.

To check the correctness of these numbers we need only recall that the number 1 stands for 1, or for 1×3, or for 1×3^2, according as it is in the unit's place or in the three's place or in the nine's place. The number 1,121 in the ternary system is changed to the decimal system as follows:

$$1,121 = 1(3^3) + 1(3^2) + 2(3) + 1 = 43 .$$

Similarly, the number 2,001,201 in the ternary system is equal to

$$2(3^6) + 1(3^3) + 2(3^2) + 1 = 1,504$$

in our decimal system and is equal to **MDIV** in the Roman (decimal) system.

To find the representation in the ternary system of the number given in the decimal system by 436, we may proceed as follows: Divide by 3 as long as is possible, writing the remainders at the side, as below:

$$
\begin{array}{r}
3\,|\,436 \\
3\,|\,\overline{145} + 1 \\
3\,|\,\overline{48} + 1 \\
3\,|\,\overline{16} + 0 \\
3\,|\,\overline{5} + 1 \\
\overline{1} + 2
\end{array}
$$

Since after five divisions by 3 the quotient is 1, we know that 3^5 is contained once in 436 and that, furthermore, 436 is smaller than 3^6. Thus the first digit in the ternary representation, reading *from left to right*, is 1. The successive remainders, in order, give the digits in order, which belong in the remaining places. The answer is 121,011.

CHECK. In the ternary system the number 121,011 is $1(3^5) + 2(3^4) + 1(3^3) + 1(3) + 1 = 436$ in our notation.

In practice, instead of writing the remainders $+1, +1, +0$, etc., as indicated above, these remainders, as soon as obtained, may be written down in their final places. But, inasmuch as they are obtained in the reverse order from the order in which they make up the number sought, they are recorded *from right to left*. An example makes this clear:

To change 645 from a number in the decimal system to a number in the ternary system, the following steps may be followed:

1) Divide 645 by 3; the quotient is 215; write down the remainder, 0, at one side.

This is the number in the unit's place, viz.......................................0.

2) Divide 215 by 3; the quotient is 71; write down the remainder, 2, at the *left* of the zero first written. We now have.......................................20.

3) Divide 71 by 3; the quotient is 23; write down the remainder, 2, at the *left* of the two digits previously written. We now have..............................220.

4) Divide 23 by 3; the quotient is 7; write down the remainder, 2, at the *left* of the three digits already obtained. We now have...............................2,220.

5) Divide 7 by 3; the quotient is 2; write down the remainder, 1, at the *left* of the four digits already found. We now have.................................12,220.

6) Division by 3 is no longer possible. The last quotient, 2, should be the first digit in the desired representation. Write it down at the left of the last number obtained. The answer is..212,220.

The reader should convince himself that 212,220 in the ternary system, $2\times3^5 + 1\times3^4 + 2\times3^3 + 2\times3^2 + 2\times3 + 0$ is equal to the number 645 in our decimal system.

Records show that certain tribes used a **duodecimal*** (base 12) system, that the Mayas of Yucatan and Central America used a **vigesimal** (base 20) system, and that the Babylonians used a **sexagesimal** (base 60) system. In more than one language the word for *five* was the word for *hand;* and among the North American Indians there were tribes for whom *ten* meant *two hands*, while *twenty* was designated by the phrase *the whole Indian*. This would indicate that a tribe which used the vigesimal system continued the counting from 10 to 20, on the toes.

The whole Indian

Why the Babylonians used a sexagesimal system is not known. Cantor† reminds us that at first the Babylonians divided the year into 360 days, and suggests that this led to the division of the circle into 360 degrees, each degree representing the daily amount of the supposed yearly revolution of the sun around the earth. They were probably familiar with the fact that in a circle a chord whose length is equal to the radius of the circle subtends an arc which is one-sixth of the circumference. This would give 60 as a convenient unit of arc and might well suggest dividing the degree into 60 parts (minutes) and the minute into 60 sec. This seems the more reasonable inasmuch as it was the Babylonians who divided the day into 24 hr., the hour into 60 min., and the minute into 60 sec.

* According to Cajori, the Romans were the first people to use a duodecimal system.

† See bibliography at end of this chapter.

Many persons maintain that a duodecimal system would be more convenient for modern life than a decimal system inasmuch as the base 12 has more divisors than the base 10.

We shall give examples showing representations of numbers in different systems. Babylonians and Mayas did not use Hindu numerals, but we use them here for convenience. A sexagesimal system needs 59 distinct symbols besides a zero, a vigesimal system needs 19, and a duodecimal system needs 11 symbols in addition to a symbol for zero *if* a principle of position be assumed. In our representation, in the examples given below, if a symbol whose value is greater than 9 is needed, it will be invented. Thus we may agree to use the Greek letters a, φ, τ, and θ,* respectively, for the numbers 10, 11, 14, and 30. We have

Decimal	*Duodecimal*	*Vigesimal*	*Sexagesimal*
18,690	12 | 18,690	20 | 18,690	60 | 18,690
	12 | 1,557	20 | 934	60 | 311
	12 | 129	20 | 46	5
	10	2	
18,690	a996	$26\tau a$	$5\varphi\theta$

It is simpler to work the other way, i.e., to change from another system to the decimal system. We give a few more examples:

Ternary,	$10,002 = 1(3^4) + 2$	$= 83$	in the *decimal* system;
Duodecimal,	$73\varphi = 7(12^2) + 3(12) + 11$	$= 1,055$	in the *decimal* system;
Vigesimal,	$73\varphi = 7(20^2) + 3(20) + 11$	$= 2,871$	in the *decimal* system;
Sexagesimal,	$73\varphi = 7(60^2) + 3(60) + 11$	$= 25,391$	in the *decimal* system;
Sexagesimal,	$730.\varphi = 7(60^2) + 3(60) + 11(\frac{1}{60}) = 25,380\frac{11}{60}$		in the *decimal* system.

If you wish a general formula, you will see that the following is correct. In it, it is assumed that the number of characters appearing on the left of the decimal point is $k+1$ and that the base of the system is b. Let the notation x_i be used for the character appearing in the $(1+i)$st place to the left of the decimal point. Then we have (using the dot between x_0 and x_{-1} to mark the place where powers of b cease and powers of $1/b$ begin)

Base b: $x_k x_{k-1} \ldots \ldots x_2 x_1 x_0 . x_{-1} x_{-2}$

$$= x_k(b^k) + x_{k-1}(b^{k-1}) + \cdots \cdots + x_2(b^2) + x_1(b) + x_0 + x_{-1}\left(\frac{1}{b}\right) + x_{-2}\left(\frac{1}{b^2}\right) + \cdots \cdots .$$

* a (alpha), φ (phi), τ (tau), θ (theta).

If you wish to test your knowledge of the processes explained above, you should solve the following problems. The answers are given on page 182.

I. Write the numbers in the decimal system which are equal to the following:

a) 4,703, duodecimal;   b) 30,065, duodecimal;   c) 229a, duodecimal;
d) 4,077, vigesimal;   e) 8,886, vigesimal;   f) 80φ, vigesimal;
g) 9,999, sexagesimal;   h) 1,100, sexagesimal;   i) 60θ, sexagesimal;
j)   10.01, binary;   k) 1,110, binary;   l) 212.02, ternary.

Note. The base of the **binary** system is 2. It has only two characters, 0 and 1. In this system the first ten numbers are 1, 10, 11, 100, 101, 110, 111, 1,000, 1,001, 1,010.

II. Find the representations in the binary and ternary systems of the numbers (a) 12, (b) 20, (c) 60, (d) 42.5, (e) 0.06.

III. Find the representations in the duodecimal, vigesimal, and sexagesimal systems of the numbers (a) 1,000, (b) 23,075, (c) 948, (d) 3,600, (e) 42.5.

4. The structure of a number system. In the preceding paragraphs it has been suggested that a number system has its beginnings in the concept of number as related to objects; that it is first associated with counting; that the acquirement by a language of number words, whether new or adapted, precedes the acquirement of number characters; that the method of enumeration seems in general to be responsible for the base of the system; and that differences in the construction and usability of number systems are due in large part to the kinds of symbols employed (i.e., to the **notation**) and to the presence or absence of the principle of position and of a zero.

Let us now look more closely at (a) the elements of the system, (b) the operations on the elements, and (c) the properties of the operations.

We shall trace the growth of the number concept of the modern child from babyhood and shall believe (and later shall show historically) that the successive stages of development represent quite well the growth in number ideas of a nation or tribe.

In the early years a child's number system consists of **positive integers** (whole numbers) only. He learns to count to 5, to count to 10, to 100, to count by two's, by five's, etc.; he learns to add, to subtract, multiply, and divide, but does not realize that his subtraction and division problems are carefully planned by the teacher so that the results are always elements of his number system, i.e., positive integers.

A brief digression here for the purpose of defining some new terms will make the following discussion easier to write and to read. Let us suppose that we have a finite or infinite **set** (or **class**) of elements, e.g., the class of all odd numbers or the class of all fractions whose denominator is 3, or the set of multiples of 5 which are not larger than 299. A class of elements is said to be **closed** under a given operation if, when the operation is performed on two arbitrary elements, the result is an element of the class. Hence, in this class of elements are found solutions to all problems which involve only this operation.

It is evident that the class of positive integers is closed under addition and also under multiplication, since the sum or product of any two positive integers is a positive integer. It is not closed under subtraction or under division, since, for example, $8 - 11$ is not a positive integer, nor is $15 \div 4$.

To summarize, the number system of the child at this stage consists of the class of *positive integers*—a class which is closed under two of the four operations mentioned.

After some skill has been acquired in the arithmetic of this number system, the system is enlarged by the addition of common **fractions**. Starting first with *proper fractions* whose introduction is motivated by the need to divide a pie, an apple, a bag of grain, or a tract of land among several persons, the child learns that two fractions, or a fraction and an integer, may be added, subtracted,* multiplied, and divided, and that the result may be a proper fraction, an improper fraction, or an integer.

The field of operation (number system) now consists of all *positive integers and positive rational fractions.* It is closed under addition, multiplication, and division but is not closed under subtraction.

An understanding of the properties of **the number 1** has been acquired gradually, i.e., the fact that the behavior of this number, the **unit** of the system, is different from that of other numbers with regard to multiplication and division. In the general case the product or quotient of two positive numbers is a *different* positive number, whereas the product or quotient of a number N by unity is the number N itself.

---

* With the same reservation as before with regard to subtraction, viz., that the problems presented have numbers so chosen that the answer is positive.

Note. The reader can see how much is concealed in this use of the letter N as a number symbol to stand for *any number* in our number system. If this procedure were not adopted, it would be necessary to write down a partial multiplication table where one of the factors is unity, e.g.,

$$2\times1=2, \qquad 5\times1=5,$$
$$3\times1=3, \qquad \ldots\ldots\ldots$$
$$4\times1=4, \qquad \ldots\ldots\ldots$$

and then to add the remark that if the reader wishes to extend the table to any number which he has in mind he will find that in every case the number on the right (the product) is the same number as the factor on the left.

This appears to be taking a great deal of pains for something which is almost trivial. In this particular instance, the feeling that it is "almost trivial" comes from the fact that we are dealing with something which is well known; the use of literal number symbols in statements not well known does not seem so trivial. In every case the formula or equation is accompanied by a statement of the range of values which each letter appearing in it may have. In the present example, N can be any number in our number system; but in the example which follows, k is restricted to be a positive integer. In every case, if the reader will give to the literal number symbol, in turn, a few of its possible values and write out the resulting numerical statement, he will begin to acquire a feeling of respect and admiration for a notation which uses little space but tells much.

EXAMPLE. The sum of the squares of the first k integers is $\frac{1}{6}k(k+1)(2k+1)$.

The number zero comes into the child's system of positive numbers at some stage of the evolution sketched above; and although it is probable that years elapse before all of the peculiar properties of this number are met and understood by the child, we pause here to mention them. This will help to complete the picture by enabling us to understand more fully the slowness of the ancients and medieval peoples in introducing a symbol and ascribing to it properties which are so unlike the properties of all other symbols of the system.

Properties of zero.

a) *Addition*, $N+0=N$, where N is any number of the system.

b) *Subtraction*, $N-0=N$.

c) *Multiplication*, $N\times0=0$.

d) *Division*, $N\div0$ *does not exist.*

Remark on (*d*): When we write $N/P=Q$ where P is *not* zero, since *"equals multiplied by equals are equal"* we may multiply both members of this equation by P and get $N=PQ$. Now let us see what happens if we *assume* that a given number, say 5, can be divided by zero. If Q is the quotient obtained by this division, we can write

$$\frac{5}{0} = Q \,,$$

and, when both sides of the equation are multiplied by zero, the result is

$$5 = 0 \,.$$

This contradiction shows that *we must not divide by zero*, since, when such division is allowed, we obtain a result which is not correct.

Let us examine the preceding more closely, for it is an instructive example of a certain type of a **mathematical proof.** It was stated in chapter 1 that every step in a mathematical proof must be a logical deduction from the original axioms, the definitions, the propositions previously proved, and any new definitions or assumptions introduced as needed. Only the multiplication axiom is used in the foregoing; but the result obtained is absurd, since 5 is not zero. Now the use of the axiom is legitimate; hence the only conclusion possible is that there is something wrong with the assumption which preceded, i.e., since there is no number Q such that $Q \times 0 = 5$, we have no right to assume that there is a Q which is the quotient of 5 by 0. This is what is meant by the phrase *"does not exist"* in (*d*).

This method of proof is not infrequent in mathematics. When a new situation arises or a new symbol is introduced, the mathematician may ask himself: "Is this formula or equation a correct mathematical statement of the situation?" or "Can this symbol be used thus and so?" In order to find a reply to his own question, he studies the logical consequences of assuming that the answer is in the affirmative. If, by a series of deductions, all justified by his axioms, definitions, and previously proved propositions, he reaches an absurd conclusion, he knows that the answer to his question cannot be the affirmative. This method of proof is called *reductio ad absurdum.*

If, on the other hand, by a series of logical steps he reaches a conclusion which is *consistent with what is already known and accepted,* and if he has confidence in his ability to reason logically, he is justified in accepting this assumption as a new relation to be added to his stock of known relations.

The next enlargement of the child's number system takes place when such numbers as $\sqrt{2}$, $\sqrt{5}$, $\sqrt[3]{3}$, etc., are met. These are called **irrational numbers,** and it is now an appropriate time for the following definitions: A number which can be written as the quotient of two integers is called a **rational number;** while an irrational number can be approximated (usually this is done in decimals which are rational numbers) as closely as we please, but cannot be written as the quotient of two integers.

Note 1. The decimal representation of an irrational number never terminates, for any terminating decimal is expressible as the quotient of two integers and is therefore rational.

EXAMPLES. $4.2136 = \dfrac{42,136}{10,000}$, $0.00215 = \dfrac{215}{100,000}$, $371.4 = \dfrac{3,714}{10}$.

Note 2. The decimal approximation of a rational number may or may not terminate.
EXAMPLES. $\frac{1}{8} = 0.125$, $\frac{1}{3} = 0.3333$ (approx.), $\frac{1}{11} = 0.090909. \ldots$.
Note 3. Whole numbers are rational numbers; e.g., 8 can be written $\frac{8}{1}$ or $\frac{16}{2}$ or $\frac{40}{5}$.

When the student has attained familiarity with the operation of **involution,** or raising to a power, the next step is to learn the inverse operation, that of extracting a root. This is called **evolution.**

Problems in involution. $1^2 = 1$, $5^2 = 25$, $3^4 = 81$, $(\frac{1}{2})^2 = \frac{1}{4}$, $(0.01)^2 = 0.0001$.

Problems in evolution. $\sqrt{9} = 3$, $\sqrt{100} = 10$, $\sqrt[3]{64} = 4$, $\sqrt[5]{32} = 2$, $\sqrt{\frac{1}{4}} = \frac{1}{2}$.

The problems above have answers that are positive rational numbers, but there are no rational numbers which are equal to $\sqrt{13}$ or $\sqrt[3]{34}$, for example.

Thus we see that unlimited extraction of roots of positive integers and positive rational fractions is not possible in a number system containing only these elements. This fact motivates another enlargement of our number system, viz., the addition of *irrational numbers.* The number system, thus enlarged, is called the **system of positive real numbers** (and zero). It is possible in this enlarged system to solve such equations as

$$x^2 - 5 = 0 \qquad \text{and} \qquad x^3 - 30 = 0 .$$

The answers are, respectively, $x = \sqrt{5}$ and $x = \sqrt[3]{30}$.

The number system of positive real numbers is closed under five of the six elementary operations with the single provision that zero must never be used as a divisor.*

The next step in the evolution of the **real number system** is the addition of *negative real numbers* to the class of positive real numbers. In this connection a true story is apropos: Little Mary was describing to her father her number exercise in the first grade at school. She explained that the teacher would hold up a card on which was written a number and that the children were expected to name the number which came *before* the one exhibited. When the teacher held up 8, the class said 7; when the teacher held up 2, the children said 1; etc. "But," said Mary, "what would we say if the teacher held up zero?" The father told her that the proper response would be -1. Mary soon was able to say that the number before -4 is -5, etc. She added the negative numbers to her number system earlier than is customary and earlier than the remaining members of her class.

Mary learns minus numbers

The introduction of negative numbers arises naturally from such ideas as 10° above zero and 10° below zero, Lat. 40° N. and Lat. 42° S., etc., but perhaps more often in connection with debts or expenditures. Usually the system of positive real numbers is adequate until elementary algebra is studied; but in this number system there are no solutions for, say, the simple linear equations

$$2x+8=0 \qquad \text{and} \qquad x+1=0 \,.$$

The number system, called **the real-number system,** now consists of zero, all positive and negative integers, all positive and negative rational fractions, and all positive and negative irrational numbers.

There is no restriction on addition, subtraction, multiplication, and involution. The only restriction on division is that *division by zero is taboo;* there is, however, a very great restriction on the extraction of roots, viz., *even-numbered roots of negative numbers cannot be expressed precisely or approximately by elements in the real-number system.* Any even power of

---

* Under which operation is this system not closed?

a positive number is a positive number, and any even power of a negative number is also a positive number; i.e., there is no positive or negative number which, when raised to an even-numbered power, is negative. On the other hand, $\sqrt[3]{-8}$ and $\sqrt[3]{-9}$ have real-number solutions. They are -2 and (approx.) -2.0801, respectively.

At each stage in the development of our number system, when a new kind of number has been met it has been given a name, and all numbers of this kind have been added to the system. Each enlargement of the system has increased its usefulness, inasmuch as problems hitherto without solution have become solvable. The name given to the last-mentioned new member of our system is **imaginary**—in fact, **pure imaginary**—the name "imaginary" and also **complex** being used for numbers which indicate the sum (or difference) of a real number and a pure imaginary number.

Pure imaginary: $\sqrt{-3}$, $\sqrt{-5}$, $\sqrt{-25}$, $\sqrt{-100}$, $3\sqrt{-1}$, $7\sqrt{-8}$.

Complex or *imaginary:* $4+\sqrt{-1}$, $3-\sqrt{-7}$, $-\frac{1}{2}+5\sqrt{-3}$, $a+b\sqrt{-1}$.

Note 1. Any pure imaginary number can be written as the product of a real number (not necessarily rational) and the square root of -1.

EXAMPLES. $\sqrt{-4}=2\sqrt{-1}$, $5\sqrt{-16}=20\sqrt{-1}$, $\sqrt{-6}=\sqrt{6}\sqrt{-1}$.

Note 2. The sum of two complex numbers is a complex number.

EXAMPLE. The sum of $7+\sqrt{-6}$ and $3-5\sqrt{-6}$ is $10-4\sqrt{-6}$.

For many purposes it is convenient to say that *every number which can be written in the form* $a+b\sqrt{-1}$, *where a and b are real numbers, is a complex number;* and this is the meaning which we shall from now on give to the term. This means that we allow b to be zero, in which case the complex number becomes a real number; in other words, *the class of all real numbers is contained in the class of all complex numbers.*

Complex numbers may be added, subtracted, multiplied, divided, or raised to a power, and there is no restriction to extracting roots.* With the single exception that division by zero is not permitted, the complex number system is closed under the elementary operations of arithmetic. Thus all problems which involve only these operations can be solved.

Complex numbers are usually met for the first time in the study of the solution of quadratic binomial equations. For example, the values of x

---

* For an explanation of the method of performing the operations of arithmetic on complex numbers, see Logsdon, *Elementary Mathematical Analysis* (New York: McGraw-Hill Book Co., Inc., 1933), Vol. II, chap. 1.

which satisfy $x^2 - 9 = 0$ are $x = 3$ and $x = -3$, while for $x^2 + 9 = 0$ the values of x are $x = 3\sqrt{-1}$ and $x = -3\sqrt{-1}$. Other examples are given in Appendix C on page 182.

5. Historical notes on the evolution of number concepts. Irrational quantities. PYTHAGORAS (born about 569 B.C.) and his students spent much time studying the right triangle. After he succeeded in proving the theorem which bears his name, viz., *The square on the hypotenuse of a right triangle is equal to the sum of the squares on the two legs*, they considered this problem: Given a number equal to the side of an isosceles right triangle, to find the number which is equal to the hypotenuse. To quote from Cajori,

The side may have been taken equal to 1, 2, 3/2, 6/5, or any other number, yet in every instance all efforts to find a number exactly equal to the hypotenuse must have remained fruitless. The problem may have been attacked again and again, until finally "some rare genius, to whom it is granted, during some happy moments, to soar with eagle's flight above the level of human thinking," grasped the happy thought that *this problem cannot be solved.* In some such manner probably arose the theory of irrational quantities, which is attributed by Eudemus to the Pythagoreans. It was indeed a thought of extraordinary boldness, to assume that straight lines could exist differing from one another not only in length,—that is, in quantity,—but also in a quality which though real was absolutely invisible. Need we wonder that the Pythagoreans saw in irrationals a deep mystery, a symbol of the unspeakable? We are told that the one who first divulged the theory of irrationals, which the Pythagoreans kept secret, perished in consequence of a shipwreck. Its discovery is ascribed to Pythagoras, but we must remember that all important Pythagorean discoveries were, according to Pythagorean custom, referred back to him. The first incommensurable ratio known seems to have been *the ratio of the side of a square to its diagonal;* this ratio is $1 : \sqrt{2}$.*

This is a *geometric concept*, inasmuch as we can at will produce two lines whose ratio is $1 : \sqrt{2}$, or any other irrational ratio expressed in square roots. In the figure on the following page are constructed a number of lines many pairs of which are **incommensurable**. This is another way of saying that they have no common unit of measure which is contained in each of them a rational number of times, or that the ratio of the lengths of such a pair of lines must contain an irrational number.

The geometry of irrationals led to an *arithmetical treatment*, viz., approximation of radicals. The Greeks found square roots much as we do

* *Op. cit.*, p. 69.

today, but their ignorance of the decimal fraction made the process of approximation very difficult.

In his tenth book Euclid treats the theory of incommensurables with a completeness not equaled by his treatment of any of the other subjects of his books. This theory remained where Euclid left it until the fifteenth century.

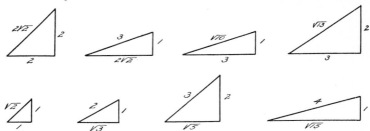

6. Historical notes. Negative quantities.

No trace of the recognition of negative numbers, as distinct from simple subtrahends, has as yet been found in the writings of the ancient Egyptians, Babylonians, Hindus, or Greeks. The Chinese made use of subtrahends at a very early date. They indicated positive coefficients by red computing rods and negative ones by black. The negative number is mentioned about 200 B.C. In the Occident the first mention of negative numbers is in the *Arithmetica of Diophantus* (about 275 A.D.), where the equation $4x + 20 = 4$ is spoken of as *absurd*.

Hindu thinking minus quantity impossible

The Indians later brought out the difference between positive and negative quantities by attaching to the one the idea of possession, to the other that of debts. They advanced beyond DIOPHANTUS in observing that *a quadratic always has two roots.* Thus BHASKARA (twelfth century after Christ) gives $x = 50$ and $x = -5$ for the roots of $x^2 - 45x = 250$. "But," says he, "the second value is, in this case, not to be taken, for it is inadequate; *people do not approve of negative roots.*" It appears as if negative roots were seen but not admitted.

In his *Ars magna* published in 1545 at Nuremberg by the great algebraist, CARDAN, we find that he takes notice of negative roots of an equation, calling them *fictitious*, while the positive roots are called *real*.

Negative numbers were not truly received into the number system until the fifteenth and sixteenth centuries.

7. **Historical notes. Imaginary quantities.** The complex roots of an equation were discussed by Cardan in the *Ars magna*. He proved that they always occur in pairs, though he failed to commit himself to any explanation as to the meaning of these "sophistic" quantities, which he said were ingenious but useless.

8. **Classification of numbers.** In the following outline of the complex-number system a classification of the elements contained in it is made showing their relations to each other. It is a number system which is adequate for solving the problems of everyday life; problems relating to buying and selling, borrowing and lending, interest, the applications of percentage, insurance, annuities, exchange of money of different nations; engineering problems of all types; the uses of electricity, the radio, wireless; transportation, time and the calendar, map-making and map interpretation; the motions of the heavenly bodies; physical phenomena— there is no possibility of completing the enumeration.

THE COMPLEX-NUMBER SYSTEM
Elements
Real numbers
Rational numbers
Integers
Rational fractions
Irrational numbers
Zero
Complex or imaginary numbers

With the aid of the foregoing outline any real number can be classified, i.e., described as to its characteristics. As examples, see the following:

$3/2$, real, rational, fraction; $3-\sqrt[4]{11}$, real, irrational;

48, real, rational, integer; $3-\sqrt[4]{-11}$, complex;

$\sqrt{4}$, real, rational, integer; $4+\sqrt[3]{-27}$, real, rational, integer;

$\sqrt{5}$, real, irrational; $4+\sqrt{-27}$, complex;

π, real, irrational; $2-\sqrt[3]{-5}$, real, irrational.

$\sqrt{-7}$, pure imaginary;

9. **The operations of arithmetic. Properties.** It seems a bit abstract to talk about the properties of the arithmetical operations; but when we consider that in mathematics there are many operations of calculus and other higher subjects whose properties differ greatly from the properties of the operations of our arithmetic, and when we consider also that there

are many arithmetics* quite unlike our arithmetic and that in many of these arithmetics the operations do not have the properties which they have in our arithmetic, it seems important to define these properties. After all, they are merely the rules of the game, and we should be able to state the rules of a game which we are playing even though we have played so long that the rules have become second nature and we hardly realize that they are there.

Three new words will be needed to describe the operations of arithmetic, viz., "commutative," "associative," and "distributive." These will now be defined and their meanings illustrated.

Commutative. An operation is called "commutative" if the result obtained by its use on two arbitrary elements taken in a certain order is the same as the result obtained by its use on the same two elements taken in the opposite order.

It is true that $8+5=5+8$, that $a+b=b+a$, where a and b are any real numbers. It is also true that $(a+b\sqrt{-1})+(c+d\sqrt{-1})=(c+d\sqrt{-1})+(a+b\sqrt{-1})$.

It is true that $8\times5=5\times8$, and that $a\times b=b\times a$, where a and b are any real numbers. The same statement holds for any two complex numbers.

It is not true that $a-b=b-a$, nor that $a\div b=b\div a$. Hence we conclude that

Addition is commutative and *multiplication is commutative.*

Associative. An operation is called "associative" if, when it is used on three or more elements, the result is independent of the manner in which they are grouped for purposes of computing. For example, *it is true* that $8+3+6=8+(3+6)=(8+3)+6=(8+6)+3$, and $8\times6\times3=(8\times6)3=8(6\times3)=(8\times3)6$. The same statements hold for complex numbers.

It is not true that $36\div(9\div3)=(36\div9)\div3$, nor that $8-(7-2)=(8-7)-2$. We conclude that

Addition is associative and *multiplication is associative.*

Distributive. *It is true* that, for all values in the complex-number system which may be given to the symbols used, we have $a(b+c-d)=ab+ac-ad$. It is this property which is meant by the statement

Multiplication is distributive with respect to addition and subtraction.

* See L. E. Dickson, *Algebras and Their Arithmetics* (Chicago: University of Chicago Press, 1923).

10. The logic of arithmetic.   In the preceding sections the beginnings of arithmetic have been traced historically—beginnings that were purely objective. The invention and use of symbols; the introduction and use of irrationals, of negative numbers, imaginary numbers, etc.—in every case there were definite needs connected with particular problems, often problems of everyday experience. This gives to arithmetic a structure which appears to be essentially different from that of Euclid's geometry, but it will presently be shown that the difference is not so great as appears at first sight.

In the development of Euclidean geometry we have (1) a **basis or foundation** consisting of a **set of assumptions called axioms,** * **postulates, or hypotheses;** (2) **definitions of new terms;** (3) **propositions or theorems** whose proofs are deduced from the assumptions and from the theorems previously proved. The assumptions are sometimes called "self-evident truths"; but this is not a good description, since, in his endeavor to reduce the number of assumptions to a minimum and to prove every proposition which could be proved, Euclid often listed as propositions and gave proofs of statements which are intuitionally evident.

In the same manner other (non-Euclidean) geometries† can be built up based on different sets of assumptions, deducing from the assumptions, a first proposition; from the assumptions and the first proposition, a second proposition; etc. The important consideration in constructing a geometry is to take care that one step follows another and that nothing not stated in the assumptions or previously proved is taken for granted.

The arithmetic whose objective development has already been described step by step *may also be constructed logically* in exactly the manner of constructing a geometry. The process is described in the following paragraphs, beginning, as before, with an arithmetic of positive integers. The reader should try to forget that he has ever heard the words "positive in-

---

* Among the axioms used in Slaught and Lennes, *Plane and Solid Geometry* (Allyn & Bacon, 1911), are the following:

  I. A figure may be moved about in space without changing its shape or size.

  II. Through two points, one and only one straight line can be drawn.

  III. If a, b, c, d are line segments such that $a=b$, $c=d$, then $a+c=b+d$ and $a-c=b-d$.

  IV. If a and b are line segments such that $a=b$, then $a\times n=b\times n$ and $a\div n=b\div n$ for any positive integer n.

  † Examples of geometries which are not Euclidean are given in chapter 8 of this book.

teger," and should take the four postulates or assumptions which follow as a description of what is meant by positive integer. The same can be said of the terms "sum," "add," "subtract," "product," etc.; each of these terms will be defined and its properties derived as an exercise in logic and *entirely apart from notions of counting or from association with objects.*

   Definition. A class of elements obeying the following four postulates will be called **the class of positive integers.**

   Postulates.

   1. *Every integer of the class has a successor.*

   2. *Every integer has, at most, one predecessor.*

   3. *There is an integer which we shall call **unity** which has no predecessor.*

   4. *The only class of integers which contains the integer unity and each of its successors is the complete class of positive integers.*

   We may choose any desired **notation**, i.e., any set of symbols and names for the symbols, to designate the integers in the class; and we may assume the principle of position or we may not assume it, as we please. The essential factor about the notation chosen is that there must be some scheme whereby we shall know how to write down the symbol which represents the successor of a given number. In what follows, the Hindu-Arabic symbols with the principle of position will be used; but the reader should be able to show that the Roman numerals or any other set of symbols satisfying the preceding condition could also be employed.

   Thus unity is represented by the symbol 1, its successor by 2, the successor of 2 by 3, etc. The last two statements are indicated notationally by the first two statements which follow:

$$1+1=2 , \qquad 2+1=3 , \qquad 3+1=4 , \qquad \ldots\ldots ,$$

with an analogous way of designating the successor of any number.

   In the second of the last equalities we may replace 2 by $1+1$ from the first equality. This gives

$$1+1+1=3 .$$

   This value of 3 may be used to replace 3 in the third of the foregoing equalities. This gives

$$1+1+1+1=4 .$$

We conclude that *by a finite number of repetitions* of this process we may succeed in writing an arbitrary number of the set as a sum of ones. A formal proof of this statement can be made by the method of mathematical induction,* which cannot be explained in this book.

The symbolic sentence $1+1=2$, which, as stated above, is chosen as the way of indicating that 2 is the successor of unity (called also *one*), is read "one plus one equals two" and also "the **sum** of one and one is two." The process of combining symbols in this manner is called **addition**. In the sentence $1+1+1=3$, the symbol 1 appears as a *summand* three times; while, when we write an arbitrary number a in a similar manner, viz., $a = 1+1+\ldots+1$, the symbol 1 will appear one more time than it appears in the analogous expression for the predecessor of a. We may then state the first theorem.

Theorem 1. Addition theorem. The sum of two positive integers is a positive integer.

We write $a+b=c$ if

$$c = \underbrace{1+1+\cdots+1}_{a \text{ summands}} + \underbrace{1+1+\cdots+1}_{b \text{ summands}} .$$

From the definition of addition the reader can easily prove† the two properties,

1. *Addition is commutative*, i.e., $a+b=b+a$.
2. *Addition is associative*, i.e., $a+(b+c)=(a+b)+c$.

The notation $c>a$ (read "c is greater than a") indicates that there is a positive integer b such that $c=a+b$. We may then write $c-a=b$ and also $c-b=a$. The operation indicated, here defined as the *inverse of addition*, is called **subtraction**.

The inequality $c>a$ is equivalent to a second inequality, $a<c$, which is read "a is less than c."

Theorem 2. Subtraction theorem. A positive integer a *may be subtracted from a positive integer* c *if and only if* c>a. *The **remainder**,* c−a, *is a positive integer.*

* Logsdon, *op. cit.*, II, 148.

† These properties were not proved on page 30. Here we have a logical proof.

The notation $a \cdot b = c$, or merely $ab = c$, is read "a multiplied by b is equal to c" and indicates that c is the positive integer obtained by adding

$$a + a + \cdots + a \qquad (b \text{ summands}),$$

or its equal

$$b + b + \cdots + b \qquad (a \text{ summands}).$$

The numbers a and b are called **factors** of c, and c is said to be the **product** of a and b.

Theorem 3. Multiplication theorem. *The product of two positive integers is a positive integer.*

If for two given integers a and c there is a positive integer b such that $ab = c$, we say that c *is divisible by* a and that the **quotient** obtained by dividing c by a is b; also, c is divisible by b with the quotient a. This process, defined as the *inverse of multiplication*, is called **division** and is indicated as follows:

$$c \div a = b, \qquad c \div b = a,$$

and also

$$\frac{c}{a} = b, \qquad \frac{c}{b} = a.$$

Theorem 4. Division theorem. *The product of two or more positive integers is divisible by each of its factors. The quotient is a positive integer.*

This completes the construction, by purely logical methods, of an arithmetic whose elements are positive integers. The theorems indicate clearly when the operations are unrestricted and under what conditions they are restricted. All problems involving only positive integers may now be solved if they have solutions in this number system. If it is desired to extend the number system to include all positive **real numbers**, it is only necessary to define positive *rational* numbers and *irrational* numbers in terms of positive integers. To do the latter we need to introduce the notion of a **limit**.

A rational number is defined as the *quotient of two integers*.

The method of defining an irrational number in terms of integers will be illustrated by $\sqrt{2}$, whose approximate value, 1.41421, is well known. Consider the following two sequences of positive rational fractions:

$$A) \quad 1, \quad \frac{14}{10}, \quad \frac{141}{100}, \quad \frac{1,414}{1,000}, \quad \frac{14,142}{10,000}, \quad \ldots, \quad a_n, \quad \ldots;$$

$$B) \quad 2, \quad \frac{15}{10}, \quad \frac{142}{100}, \quad \frac{1,415}{1,000}, \quad \frac{14,143}{10,000}, \quad \ldots, \quad b_n, \quad \ldots.$$

The two sequences can be extended indefinitely by the process of extracting square root. They have the following properties:

First. No term in sequence (A) is smaller than the term which precedes it or larger than *any* term in sequence (B).

Second. No term in sequence (B) is larger than the term which precedes it or smaller than *any* term in sequence (A).

As the number of terms in the two sequences increases, the values of the last terms written down, indicated by a_n in the one case and by b_n in the other, satisfy the inequalities

$$b_n > \sqrt{2} > a_n .$$

Moreover, *by taking* n *sufficiently large*, the differences $b_n - \sqrt{2}$ and $\sqrt{2} - a_n$ may be made less than any small number previously written down; $\sqrt{2}$ *is said to be* **the limit of the sequence** (A) *and also* **the limit of the sequence** (B). Thus, in the two separate cases *the irrational number is* **defined** *as the limit of an infinite sequence of rational numbers.* In the same way, every irrational number can be defined in terms of infinite sequences of rational numbers, though the method of obtaining the sequences is not always as simple as the one above.

If now we introduce a new symbol, say 0, and call it the predecessor of 1 and another symbol, -1, as the predecessor of 0, we have all that is needed to extend the system of *positive* real numbers to the system of *all* real numbers. We define "addition," "subtraction," "multiplication," and "division" for elements which are all negative or for elements some of which are positive and some negative. No difficulty arises for addition and subtraction, but it is *purely arbitrary* to say:

1. The product (quotient) of a positive number by a negative number is a negative number, and

2. The product (quotient) of two negative numbers is a positive number.

Thus, from the assumptions and definitions we have built up the real-number system with its operations and their properties from a purely logical point of view. Not once did we associate numbers with objects or with counting; nor, for example, did we associate division with partition of a set of objects. This number system is purely a brain child.

11. Early arithmetic. It is not possible here to give an exhaustive account of the arithmetic used by all of the important tribes of ancient times or even a partial account of their accomplishments. We shall content ourselves with a brief recountal of the most important facts concerning the arithmetic of the Babylonians, the Egyptians, the Mayas, Hindus, Greeks, and Romans. The first three of these nations flourished before 2000 B.C., after which they made little or no scientific progress; the Hindus, centuries before the Christian Era, showed a great fondness for calculating with large numbers and throughout ancient and medieval times kept alive their interest in the science, from time to time obtaining new number ideas as well as simplification in method of operation. Their influence on the arithmetic of the twentieth century is incalculable.

The ancient Greek and Roman civilizations extend roughly over the period from the tenth century before Christ to the fourth century after Christ.

BABYLONIANS

The Babylonians had two distinct number systems, decimal and sexagesimal, in both of which they used wedge-shaped characters, the so-called **cuneiform** writing, made in soft clay with a pointed stick called a **stylus.** Tablets to be preserved were baked. Only in the last century have the scholars been able to decipher the cuneiform writing of the Babylonians and the hieroglyphics of the Egyptians.

In both systems the additive principle up to nine repetitions is used. The principle of position appears in the sexagesimal system several thousand years before it is found in their decimal system, where it appears to have been introduced about the fifth or sixth century after Christ. Likewise, there is no record of a zero in the decimal system, though a zero symbol ⚹ was used in the sexagesimal system several centuries before the Christian Era.

The following symbols represent the same number in both systems:

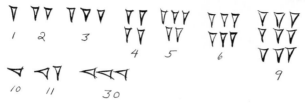

while for the base 60 we find

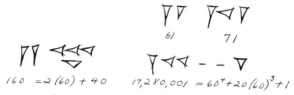

$$160 = 2(60) + 40 \qquad 17,280,001 = 60^4 + 20(60)^3 + 1$$

Babylonian cuneiform number characters

The fame of the Babylonians as indefatigable and accurate investigators of the course of the stars is attested by Pliny the Elder (first century after Christ), who fixes the beginnings of their observations at 100,000 B.C. In the study of the celestial universe, says Loria in *Storia delle Mathematiche*,*

Babylonians as astrologers

They were not moved entirely by the disinterested desire to discover the laws governing the motions of the sun and of the stars, but by the tormenting desire to discover important announcements of future events: whence here for the first time is apparent a fact, many times met in the course of centuries, viz., that lies and deception (which characterize astrology) give life to one of the disciplines (astronomy) constituting a reason for pride of the human spirit.

An important source of our information regarding the mathematics of the Babylonians is a number of tablets, called the Table of Senkreh,

* Vol. I. Turin: Sten, 1929.

discovered in 1854 by Loftus on the banks of the Euphrates. These tablets date back to 2300–1600 B.C. and contain, among other things, a table of squares of the numbers 1, 2, 3, ... , 60, and a table of cubes of 1, 2, 3, ... , 30. The squares read easily up to "7² is 49." For the square of 8 the tablet gives ⅴ₩₩, which can be correct only if the first symbol stands for 60, i.e., one in the sixties' place. The same system is followed throughout the tables of squares and cubes. Parts of an old Babylonian multiplication table have also been found with integers arranged in columns up to 180,000 and division tables up to 12,960,000. The Babylonians established a complete system of weights and measures and were undoubtedly the best bookkeepers of antiquity. From their detailed records of purchases, sales, wages paid to men, women, and children we get a fairly comprehensive idea of economic conditions among them.

EGYPTIANS

The Egyptians had a purely decimal system with no zero and no principle of position; their writing was picture writing, or **hieroglyphics.**

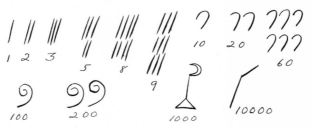

Egyptian hieroglyphics

The symbol for 100 may be a surveyor's chain, 100 units in length. The symbol for 1,000 represents the lotus flower; for 10,000, a pointed finger was drawn; and for 100,000, a fish. For 1,000,000 there was a picture of a man holding up both hands, perhaps in astonishment at the use of a number so great.

Egypt has the distinction of having given to the modern world *the oldest mathematical document extant.* It is called the Rhind Papyrus, was found at Thebes in Egypt about eighty years ago, and is now in the British Museum. It is a single roll 18½ ft. in length and 13 in. high; was written by AHMES, a scribe, sometime between 2,000 and 1,700 B.C.; and purports to be a copy of an older manuscript. It is believed to give us knowledge of the mathematical attainments of the Egyptians as far back as 3,000 B.C. It is a hand book (corresponding to our hand books of tables and formulas) containing two distinct parts. In the first part, fractions whose numerators are 2 are broken up into sums of proper fractions each having unity for numerator, e.g., $2/21 = 1/14+1/42$. Ahmes writes the result (in hieroglyphics), omitting the sign of addition, $1/14$ $1/42$. Among the hundreds of fractions in his list the only one with numerator 2 to which he did not apply the decomposition process was $2/3$. For some reason he was willing to leave this fraction with a numerator not unity.

Ahmes and papyrus

In multiplication he used a process of doubling. For example, the product of 13×37 might be obtained by either of the two following processes:

1′	13′		1′	37′
2	26		2	74
4′	52′		4′	148′
8	104		8′	296′
16	208		—	—
32′	416′		13	481
—	—			
37	481			

The numbers primed in the left column add up to the multiplier; the primed numbers in the second column add up to the product.

In the second part of the Rhind Papyrus are given solutions of problems of everyday life. There are problems on the baking of bread, stuffing of geese for market, paying of laborers, selling of grain, problems on the pyramids, etc. In problems requiring algebraic analysis, the unknown was always denoted by the word *hau*, whose best translation seems to be "heap." We have (Cantor):

Heap, its seventh, its whole makes 19 ,

i.e., $x/7+x=19$.

To give an idea of the phraseology used in stating problems, the following is taken from the translation of the papyrus which was published by the Mathematical Association of America in 1927: "Go down I times 3 into the hekat measure, 1/3 of me is added to me, 1/3 of 1/3 of me is added to me, 1/9 of me is added to me; return I, filled am I."

Ahmes gives to π a value equal to $(16/9)^2 = 3.1604$. The papyrus is inscribed: **"Direction for knowing all dark things."**

MAYAS

The Mayas of Yucatan about the beginning of the Christian Era had a highly developed vigesimal (base 20) system in which they made the earliest known application of a symbol for zero and the principle of posi-

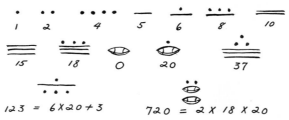

Maya notation

tion.* They had separate words for 20; for 20^2, or 400; and for 20^3, or 8,000. A symbol representing a number whose value is greater than 20

Maya and stone carving

must be read vertically, from the top down, instead of from left to right as in our notation. The second position is the twenties' place, but the third position represents 18×20 instead of 20×20. The former was more convenient for calendar use, inasmuch as the Maya year contained 18 months of 20 days each with five extra holidays at the end of each year.

The Mayas were an American Indian tribe living in Yucatan and parts of Central America and Mexico at the time of the Spanish Conquest. We have found their hieroglyphic writing on the walls of buildings recently excavated and in a few of their sacred books not destroyed by the Spaniards. Our stock of knowledge of this remarkable people is growing year by year as more and more evidences of their civilization are uncovered.

* Cajori, *op. cit.*, p. 159.

GREEKS

The Greeks had two distinct notations for numbers: the one consisted of a set of symbols associated with the first letters of the number words; the other was an alphabetic system, introduced about 500 B.C., in which the twenty-four letters of the alphabet plus three archaic letters were used to represent the numbers 1, 2, ... , 9, 10, 20, ... , 90, 100, 200, ... , 900. The additive principle was used only up to four repetitions.

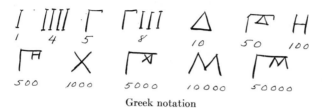

Greek notation

Neither of the notation systems of the Greeks (or the system of Roman numerals) lends itself easily to computation, and it is not surprising that little numerical arithmetic was added by them to that which they received from the Arabs. The Greeks were philosophers and were greatly interested in the philosophic aspects of mathematics; indeed, we are told that mathematics had first place in the ancient schools of philosophy.

PYTHAGORAS, a Phoenician, born about 569 B.C., visited Egypt and acquainted himself with the learning of the Egyptian priests, who were said to devote not less than twenty-two years to the study of geometry and astronomy. Later he established himself at Crotona in Magna Graecia in 530 B.C., where he opened a school which, after a slow start,

Pythagoreans studying theorem

was crowded with enthusiastic audiences; citizens of all ranks, especially those of the upper classes, attended and even the women broke a law which forbade their going to public meetings and flocked to hear him. Among his most attentive auditors was Theano, the young and beautiful daughter of his host Milo, whom, in spite of the disparity of their ages, he married.*

* The quotation is from W. W. R. Ball, *A Short Account of the History of Mathematics* (London: Macmillan & Co., 1919).

With the more intellectual of his followers, the Pythagoreans, he formed a brotherhood which shared all things in common from the simplest details of their rugged and severely disciplined living, their personal possessions and political beliefs, to their intellectual achievements. It was a rule of the organization that the glory of any fresh discovery should be ascribed to Pythagoras himself, that no new knowledge should be published but should be transmitted verbally to members only. It is said that Hippasus was drowned for violating his oath by publicly boasting that he had added the dodecahedron to the number of regular solids enumerated by the Pythagoreans.

The mathematical subjects with which they dealt were divided into four categories: number absolute, or *arithmetic;* number applied, or *music;* magnitudes at rest, or *geometry;* and magnitudes in motion, or *astronomy. This* quadrivium *was long considered the necessary and sufficient course of study for a liberal education.*

We cannot go more deeply into their theories but must not leave Pythagoras without recalling that to him is given credit for the first proof of the proposition which bears his name, viz., *The square on the hypotenuse of a right-angled triangle is equal to the sum of the squares on the two legs.* Though perhaps no proof had been made ere this, the theorem was by no means new. An old Babylonian inscription recently translated shows that it was known in the first dynasty of Babylon under Hammurabi, about 2100 B.C.

The Pythagorean school flourished many decades after the tragic end of its leader.

A second important mathematical center of the Greeks was at Alexandria in Egypt. The school was established and supported by Ptolemy I and his successors. It flourished as a school of science, mathematics, literature, and philosophy during the three centuries immediately preceding the Christian Era. Among the great scholars at Alexandria were:

EUCLID, who wrote the first systematic treatment of geometry;

ERATOSTHENES, who computed the size of the earth, constructed a calendar which became the basis of later calendars, and who wrote a geography;

ARISTARCHUS, who measured the sun and the moon;

APOLLONIUS, who wrote a treatise on conic sections;

HIPPARCHUS, who computed the length of the tropical year, obtaining a value which differs from the true value by less than 6 min.; and

HYPATIA, the first woman mathematician of whom we have knowledge. At the death of her father, Theon, she was elected head of the school. Equally famous as philosopher and mathematician, her sad end is related in Kingsley's novel *Hypatia*.

ROMANS

The Romans used a decimal system for integers; but their fractions were duodecimal, i.e., powers and aliquot parts of 1/12. They had no zero and no principle of position, but introduced a slight notational simplification, the *subtractive principle*, e.g., IV and CM. The arithmetic of the Romans had a purely practical turn. They left a mass of quite complicated problems arising from controversies regarding questions of inheritance, of private property, and of reimbursement of interest. No real mathematical advance is found anywhere in Roman history; in fact, it not infrequently happened that they muddled hopelessly mathematics which they had inherited from the Greeks.

HINDUS

The numerals 1, 2, ... , 9 used in almost all parts of the globe are directly traceable to nine Sanskrit characters used in ancient times by the Hindus, transmitted, with a zero* acquired later, to the Arabs, who modified them somewhat and introduced them into Europe by way of Spain in the eighth century. The Hindus loved calculation for its own sake and could certainly not have indulged their passion if they had not had at hand a system of notation with the characteristics of simplicity, position-value, and a zero.

We are indebted to the Arabs also for our knowledge of the Hindu processes and problems, for no early Hindu treatises have been preserved. Throughout the Dark Ages the Arabs were the most serious students in the world; they kept the torch of learning aglow while Europe was in darkness. About 925 A.D., MAHAVIR in his *Arithmetic* states the topics of his

Arabs were students

subject in a manner characteristic of the time and people. He says:

* Cf. p. 14.

With the help of the accomplished holy sages, who are worthy to be worshiped by the lords of the world, and of their disciples and disciples' disciples, who constitute the well-known jointed series of preceptors, I glean from the great ocean of the knowledge of numbers in the manner in which gems are (picked up) from the sea, gold is from the stony rock and the pearl is from the oyster shell; and give out, according to the power of my intelligence, the Sarasangraha, a small work on arithmetic which is not small in value.

Accordingly, from this ocean of Sarasangraha, which is filled with the water of terminology and has the arithmetical operations for its bank; which is full of the bold rolling fish represented by the operations relating to fractions, and is characterized by the great crocodile represented by the chapter of miscellaneous examples; which is possessed of the waves represented by the chapter on the rule-of-three, and is variegated in splendor through the luster of the gems represented by the excellent language relating to the chapter on mixed problems; and which possesses the extensive bottom represented by the chapter on area problems, and has the sands represented by the chapter on the cubic contents of excavations; and wherein shines forth the advancing tide represented by the chapter on shadows, which is related to the department of practical calculation in astronomy—(from this ocean) arithmeticians possessing the necessary qualifications in abundance will, through the instrumentality of calculation, obtain such pure gems as they desire.*

Mahavir has numerous problems resulting in strings of units† and zeros, with a kind of play on the zero; e.g.,

In this problem write down 3, 4, 1, 7, 8, 2, 4, and 1 (in order from the units' place upwards), and multiply by 7; and then say that it is the necklace of precious gems. *Ans. 100,010,001.*

Write down (the number) 142857143, and multiply it by 7; and then say that it is the royal necklace. *Ans. 1,000,000,001.*

Numerous translations of the arithmetic of the Arabs were made into Latin, the language of the universities. From these we learn how far-reaching and complicated were the applications which they made of their arithmetic to the problems of their everyday experiences.

12. Computing machines. Attention has been called to the fact that the early number characters were unsuited to calculation. Also, at first there were no convenient writing materials. Papyrus was unknown in

---

* M. RAṄGACARYA, *The Gaṇita-Sara-Sangraha of Mahaviracarya*, with English translation and notes (Madras, 1912), pp. 3–4.

† *Ibid.*, p. 11.

Greece before the seventh century before Christ, and paper is a comparatively recent product. (The latter may have been brought into Europe by
the Moors, although specimens dating from about the year 1 have been
found on the eastern borders of China.) Tablets of clay or wax were not
suited for calculation. Of necessity, a computing machine was devised.
It was called the **abacus.**

The first abacus was a dust abacus, a table of dust or sand. On it
computing was done with a stick or stylus, and erasing consisted in
smoothing out the dust or sand with the hand. Next was used a ruled
table with small sticks, pebbles, or counters arranged in lines. Using the
principle of position, a single counter in a certain line would represent 1, in
another line it would represent 10 (if 10 is the base of the number system),
while in another line it would represent 1/10. The Romans, as previously
mentioned, used the lines representing integers for powers of 10, while
on the lines on which they represented their fractions, counters indicated multiples of powers of 1/12 instead of powers of 1/10, as might be
expected.

The ruled table was in common use in Europe until the opening of the
seventeenth century, and much later than that
in various other localities, e.g., India, Mesopo-
tamia, and Egypt.

A later form of the abacus consists of a frame
on which are stretched wires carrying movable
beads or disks. This form is still found in Russia,
Persia, China, Japan, and parts of India. In

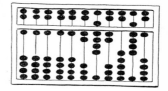

Abacus

China it is called the **swan pan** (suan pan); and with some experience it
is possible to add, subtract, multiply, and divide more rapidly with the
swan pan than with paper and pencil.

The abacus is frequently mentioned in early Greek and Latin writings. It is the earliest form of the computing machine. Later forms relieve
computers of an untold amount of drudgery.

There are now electrical machines which perform all of the operations
of arithmetic. They add and subtract as rapidly as numbers can be put
into the machine. The quotient to ten digits of a number having ten
digits or less divided by a number having ten digits or less can be obtained

in less than 15 sec. The same is true of multiplication. After the numbers are put into the machine, division is entirely automatic; but multiplication is usually done by hand. A square root can be obtained correct to ten places in about $2\frac{1}{2}$ min. The cumulative sums of seventy-five individual products in which one of the multipliers of each product has three digits can be secured in about 6 min.

The latest models of calculators are small compact machines weighing less than 20 lb.

There are also planimeters, integraphs, harmonic analyzers, etc., which perform the operations of the calculus.

It has taken many pages to present this very sketchy and incomplete account of the development of our number system and notation with some mention of the manner of treatment of certain problems solved by early peoples. A second chapter quite as lengthy could be written in which would be traced the evolution of our operational symbols, $+$, $-$, ... , etc. We shall not undertake to do this* but shall proceed with some remarks concerning the development and uses of algebra.

BIBLIOGRAPHY

G. J. Allman, *Greek Geometry from Thales to Euclid.* Dublin: Hodges, Fidgis & Co., 1889.
W. W. R. Ball, *A Short Account of the History of Mathematics.* London: Macmillan & Co., 1919.
F. Cajori, *A History of Mathematics.* New York: Macmillan Co., 1909.
F. Cajori, *A History of Mathematical Notations.* Chicago: Open Court Publishing Co., 1928.
N. B. Cantor, *Vorlesungen über Geschichte der Mathematik.* Leipzig: Teubner, 1892–98.
K. Fink, *Geschichte der Elementar Mathematik.* Translated by Beman and Smith. Chicago: Open Court Publishing Co., 1900.
T. L. Heath, *A History of Greek Mathematics.* 2 vols. Oxford, 1921.
L. C. Karpinski, *The History of Arithmetic.* New York: Rand, McNally & Co., 1925.
G. Loria, *Storia delle Matamatiche*, Vol. 1. Turin: Sten, 1928.
Rhind Mathematical Papyrus, photographed, translated, and printed by the Mathematical Association of America, 1927.
An excellent bibliography for supplementary reading is given on pp. 36 and 37 of Karpinski's *The History of Arithmetic.*

* For a scholarly exposition of this subject see *A History of Mathematical Notations* by Florian Cajori (Chicago: Open Court Publishing Co., 1928).

CHAPTER 3

ALGEBRA

THE subject of algebra is likely to be viewed with disfavor by the non-mathematician because of the fact that to a considerable degree it appears to be devoted to formal manipulation. A surgeon, on preparing to perform an important and dangerous operation, would not be thrilled by setting out all of his tools, rubbing them up, getting them sterilized and the knives sharpened; but it is rather important that these routine details be attended to. To continue the comparison with surgery, one eminent surgeon wished to further the spread of elementary surgical instruction. "The higher mathematics," said he, "will not help you to bind up a broken leg." This is indeed true, but it is also true that surgery does not help one to add up accounts, or to think logically, or to accomplish the closely related feat of understanding a joke.

To the word "algebra" may be attributed *the significance of a science which arranges in methodical order the steps needed to solve problems* with given numbers and letters (used as number symbols), one or more of which may represent unknown quantities, and also *justifies the steps of the solution*. In other words, algebra provides not only a method but the reasons for the method.

1. Form. According to Nesselmann, there have been three distinct phases in the development of algebra. These phases are described as follows:

A. In the first stage algebra can be called *rhetorical*, because, lacking any kind of symbol, the calculations are effected by words. Most of the writings of the very early peoples, as well as those of the Greek arithmeticians of the neo-Platonic and the non-Pythagorean schools, belong to this first species of algebra.

B. In its second stage algebra can be called *syncopated*, because it uses words interspersed here and there with abbreviations to make simpler and more rapid the progress of the reasoning and of the calculations; it was Diophantus who initiated this phase.

C. In the last—and, we may feel safe in saying, almost perfect—stage of development algebra can be called *symbolic*, because it uses special symbols to indicate the given and the unknown quantities and it also represents the various operations by operational symbols. Words have entirely disappeared from the steps of an algebraic proof or solution, though they may be used in explaining the process. Not until the seventeenth century did algebra reach a stage nearing that of perfection as regards symbolic representation.

2. Importance of symbolism. Two ends of exceeding great importance are attained by the use of symbolism (called also **notation**)—ends themselves entirely different but of such great significance that either one alone would not only justify the use of symbolic algebra but would actually make it imperative. These advantages will be discussed in turn.

A. *Saving of time and labor.* By use of number symbols, general formulas are written which may be employed in solving hundreds and thousands of special numerical cases. An example which will be studied in detail in section 4 is that of the general quadratic equation. An equation in a single unknown, say x, is called a **quadratic equation** if it contains an x^2 term but no term in x^3, x^4, ... x^n where $n > 2$. There may or may not be present a term in x or a *constant term* (a term not containing any power of x). We can write down any number of **special quadratic equations**, i.e., equations with *numerical coefficients* in the three possible terms. E.g.,

$$\text{i)} \qquad x^2 - 5x + 5 = 0 ,$$
$$\text{ii)} \qquad 2x^2 + x - 3 = 0 ,$$
$$\text{iii)} \quad -4x^2 - 2x + 7 = 0 ,$$
$$\text{iv)} \qquad 3x^2 - 15 = 0 ,$$
$$\text{v)} \qquad x^2 + 10x = 0 ,$$

A quadratic equation in which letters, instead of numbers, appear in the three terms, viz.,

$$ax^2 + bx + c = 0, \qquad (a \neq 0),$$

is called a **general quadratic equation.** A special quadratic is obtained from the general quadratic by giving numerical values to the number symbols a, b, and c. Moreover, all real quadratics are obtained in this way.

A way of solving* a quadratic equation is by use of the **method of completing the square** (cf. sec. 4). By applying this method in turn to the quadratics (i)–(v) on the last page, the two solutions of each equation may be obtained. Exactly the same method (completing the square) when applied to the general quadratic gives a **formula** for the two roots, a formula which contains only the symbols a, b, c and symbols of the operations of arithmetic. This formula is (cf. p. 54),

$$x = \frac{-b \pm \sqrt{b^2 - 4ac}}{2a},$$

one root of the equation being obtained by using the plus sign before the sign of the radical, the other by using the minus sign.

Let us suppose now that it is desired to use this formula to obtain the roots of (i) above. Comparing $x^2 - 5x + 5 = 0$ with $ax^2 + bx + c = 0$, we see that to get our special quadratic (i) from the general quadratic we must set $a = 1, b = -5$, and $c = 5$. Hence, to get the roots of our special quadratic

---

* *To solve an equation* containing a single variable (unknown), say x, is to find all numbers and number symbols each of which, on being substituted for x in the equation, makes the two members of the equation reduce to the same number. These values of x are called **solutions** of the equation and are also called **roots** of the equation. For example, 5 is a root of the equation $x^2 - 2x = 15$, for, when 5 is substituted for x, the result is $25 - 10 = 15$, a true relation for the numbers. Also, -3 is a root of the same equation, since $(-3)^2 - 2(-3) = 15$.

The next paragraph shows that *every quadratic equation has* **two** *roots* or solutions. It is proved in higher algebra that *a cubic equation in one unknown has* **three** *roots*, that *a quartic equation in one unknown has* **four** *roots*, that *an n-ic equation in one unknown has* **n** *roots*. This is called the **fundamental theorem of algebra,** and it cannot be proved in a simple manner.

When an equation has two or more unknowns, a solution consists of as many numbers as there are unknowns. For example, one solution of $4x^2 + 3y = 1$ is $x = 2, y = -5$; another solution is $x = 1, y = -1$. For brevity, these two solutions are often written $(2, -5)$ and $(1, -1)$, respectively. Such an equation has an infinite number of solutions. They are discussed more fully in section 3 of this chapter. The word "root" is an alternative word for "solution" *only* when there is a *single unknown* in the equation.

from those of the general quadratic, we must, in the formula given above, make the same replacement, $a=1$, $b=-5$, and $c=5$. This gives

$$x = \frac{5 \pm \sqrt{25-20}}{2} = \frac{5 \pm \sqrt{5}}{2}.$$

Thus the two roots* of $x^2-5x+5=0$ are $x=\dfrac{5+\sqrt{5}}{2}$ and $x=\dfrac{5-\sqrt{5}}{2}$.

A little practice in replacing the symbols a, b, and c by numerical values enables us to write out the two roots of each of a dozen or more special quadratics in less time than it would take to go through the process of completing the square for any one of them.

This is only one instance of a multitude of general formulas which have been found such that, once understood, they may forever after be used for special cases merely by replacing letters used as number symbols by numerical values. For this reason, early in a course in algebra students are assigned the task of learning to substitute numbers for letters and perform indicated operations of arithmetic. It is amazing how inaccurate college students are in this elementary exercise.

Thus the use of a general formula is a great labor-saver as well as a time-saver.

B. Scientific progress. When the relations between known and unknown quantities are displayed in a compact formula, or in an equation, or in a system of equations, where the symbols used are simple and suggestive, the mind, through the eye, can "take in" these relationships more rapidly—and, what is of even greater importance, more effectively—than is possible if complicated relations are expressed in long, involved sentences. The broader the perspective, the better is the understanding, and the more readily can the mind reach out in search of *new relations and properties.* Mention has already been made of the fact that perhaps the chief reason that the early Romans did not create any arithmetic of consequence was because their notation was clumsy and awkward. A second illustration of this *dependence of scientific advance on notation* is found in the story of the invention and development of the calculus.

The calculus was invented ("invented" is the correct word to use

---

* The roots given in the text are *precise*, and they cannot be given precisely without the use of a radical sign. Their *approximate values* are 4.7361 and 0.2639.

inasmuch as *the calculus is a method* rather than a fact) independently by the great Englishman, SIR ISAAC NEWTON (1642–1727), and the also great German, GOTTFRIED WILHELM LEIBNIZ (1646–1716). Newton's work antedates that of Leibniz by about ten years, but the latter published an account of what he was doing before Newton's work was made known to any except a small circle of his friends and their correspondents. For fifteen years Leibniz was acclaimed as the inventor of the calculus, after which time certain of Newton's friends let it be known that it was their belief that Leibniz had "borrowed" some of his ideas from Newton. This excited Leibniz' friends, and thus was opened a series of undignified and ungrounded accusations and recriminations from both sides. It is now generally believed that the results which Leibniz published were entirely his own work, but there were two consequences of the controversy which had far-reaching effects on the development of mathematics. One was the initiation by Leibniz of the recurring practice of issuing *challenge problems*. As first they were intended merely as exercises in the new calculus, but later they often took on the nature of defiances. The second effect was more to be deplored: the controversy produced a long and bitter alienation between English and Continental mathematicians, stopping almost completely all interchange of ideas. Unfortunately for the English, the notation which Newton adopted was awkward and clumsy, while Leibniz had chosen a symbolism well adapted to express the ideas and processes involved. The result was that the Germans made rapid progress in extending the scope of applications of the differential and integral calculus, while, not only did the English lag in their discoveries, but they were not even aware that the Germans were outdistancing them. Not until 1820 did the English realize what remarkable contributions to the world's mathematical knowledge the Germans had made; they then adopted the simpler notation and were able to assist in making further advances in the development and applications of the subject.

3. The equation. There is probably no one word which is more closely associated in everyone's mind with the mathematician than the word **equation**. The reason for this is easy to find. In the language of mathematics the word "equation" plays the same rôle as that played by the word "sentence" in a spoken and written language. Now *the sentence is the* *unit for the expression of thought; the equation is the unit for the expression of a mathematical idea.*

In the spoken and written language a *declarative sentence* states a fact, i.e., expresses an idea, while an *interrogative sentence* asks a question. In the language of mathematics an **identical equation** states a mathematical fact, i.e., a relation which is always and unconditionally true, while a **conditional equation** asks the questions: (*a*) Is this relationship ever true? (*b*) If so, what value or values must the symbols which appear in it have in order that it may be a true relationship?

In the first footnote in section 2 it was stated that any value or set of values of the variables appearing in an equation which makes the two members of the equation identical is called a *solution* of the equation. We shall inquire into some of the principles involved in solving equations; and we can be certain, in advance, that as far as his present knowledge enables him to do so, the mathematician has devised a means of classifying equations and finding formulas for solving them. By so doing, one formula provides the solution for a great many equations, thus reducing as much as is possible the labor of computing.

Following are some examples of identical and conditional equations:

Identical equations:

(1) $3x+5-x+1=2x+6$,

(2) $x^2-9=(x-3)(x+3)$.

Conditional equations:

(3) $3x-6=0$,   ($x=2$ is the only solution.)

(4) $x^2=x+12$,   ($x=4$ and $x=-3$ are both solutions.)

(5) $4x-3+3y=5+3x-2y$.   (There are many solutions.)

Of the conditional equations, (3) and (4) are called **determinate equations** while (5) is called **indeterminate**. It has an infinite number of solutions, but it is not an identity like (1) and (2). It is equivalent to the equation $y=8/5-x/5$, some of whose solutions are

$$x=3 ,\qquad y=1 ;\qquad x=13 ,\quad y=-1 ;\qquad x=2 ,\quad y=\tfrac{6}{5} ;$$
$$x=-2 ,\quad y=2 ;\qquad x=7 ,\quad y=\tfrac{1}{5} ;\qquad x=\tfrac{1}{2} ,\quad y=\tfrac{3}{2} .$$

Any equation containing two or more unknowns is necessarily indeterminate if complex numbers are allowed as solutions, but it is easy to
find equations in two or more unknowns which have a finite number of
real solutions. As an example, the only real solution of $x^2+y^2+z^2=0$ is
$x=0$, $y=0$, $z=0$. It is likewise easy to find equations which are indeterminate in the real-number system but determinate in the system of positive integers.

EXAMPLE. Mary has two dollars in dimes and quarters. How many pieces of money
has she?

SOLUTION. Let $x=$ the number of dimes and $y=$ the number of quarters. Then $10x+$
$25y=200$ (cents). Since x and y may have no values other than positive integers and zero,
the only solutions possible are $(x, y)=(20, 0)$, $(15, 2)$, $(10, 4)$, $(5, 6)$, $(0, 8)$, five solutions
in all.

The equation $10x+25y=200$ may be written $y=8-2x/5$. If *all real
solutions* are allowed, the equation is *indeterminate*, since for every real x
there is a corresponding real y. However, when the solutions are required
to be positive integers, the only ones are the pairs of numbers listed above.
Hence the query, "How many dimes and quarters has Mary?" is equivalent to the query, "What solutions has the equation $10x+25y=200$ in the
number system of positive integers?"

Many problems involving the same principles could be given, e.g., (1) A farmer has
$300 which he wishes to invest in lambs and calves. The lambs are worth $8.00 each, and
the calves are worth $20 each. How many can he buy? (2) It is desired to buy bonds of
three companies; bonds (par value $100) of Company A sell at $45, bonds of Company B
at $70, and bonds of Company C at $105. These bonds can be bought in denominations
of $100, $500, and $1,000 (par value). How can an investment of $12,000 be made? (See
page 183 for answers.)

In these and similar problems the mathematician sets up his equation
and asks himself the question, "What are the solutions of these equations
in positive integers?" He abstracts himself from the notions of dimes,
quarters, lambs, calves, bonds, and seeks a method for solving an indeterminate linear equation in positive integers. In other words, he recog-
nizes that there is a large class of indeterminate equations with this one
thing in common, viz., the necessity of determining all solutions in *positive
integers*. A method, once devised, is ready for use not only in the one or
several problems which motivated its investigation but in all other problems of the same type.

4. Solution of real equations by formula. When all of the coefficients which appear in an equation are real numbers, the equation is called a **real equation.** We shall study only real equations in this book.

A **linear equation** in a single unknown contains a term or terms in the first power of that unknown but no term in a higher power. It may or may not contain constants different from zero. After like terms are combined, a linear equation in x can always be written in the following form,

$$ax+b=0,$$

where a is not zero. There is one and only one solution of this equation; it is given by the formula

$$x=\frac{-b}{a},$$

which becomes $x=0$ if $b=0$. Thus the formula for solving a general linear equation is a very simple one in which the only operations to be performed are (1) change of sign and (2) division. When the equation is real, the solution is a real number.

The formula for the solution of the *general quadratic equation*

$$ax^2+bx+c=0,$$

discussed in section 2 above, is obtained by the following steps:

(i) Subtract c from both members of the equation and get

$$ax^2+bx=-c.$$

(ii) Multiply both members of the equation by $4a$. This gives

$$4a^2x^2+4abx=-4ac.$$

(iii) Add b^2 to both members. This completes the square on the left.

$$4a^2x^2+4abx+b^2=b^2-4ac.$$

(iv) Re-write the first member as a square.

$$(2ax+b)^2=b^2-4ac.$$

(v) Take the square root of both members; it can only be indicated on the right, as follows:

$$(2ax+b)=\pm\sqrt{b^2-4ac}.$$

(vi) Subtract b from both members. This leaves

$$2ax=-b\pm\sqrt{b^2-4ac}.$$

(vii) Divide by the coefficient of x and get the quadratic formula,

$$x=\frac{-b\pm\sqrt{b^2-4ac}}{2a}.$$

In this case it is not true that the solutions are always real when the equation is real. This is evident from the fact that, when numerical values are substituted for a, b, and c in the formula, a square root is to be taken, viz., $\sqrt{b^2-4ac}$. Three situations are possible: first, b^2-4ac *is a positive number*, in which case the equation has *two different real solutions*, one obtained by use of the positive sign before the radical sign in the formula and the other by use of the negative sign; second, b^2-4ac *has the value zero*, in which case we may say that the equation has *two real and equal roots;* third, b^2-4ac *is a negative number*, in which case *the two roots of the equation are complex numbers*, not real. Thus the number

$$b^2-4ac$$

bears a very important relation to the two roots of the given quadratic equation—in fact, it tells the **nature of the roots**. It is called the **discriminant of the equation.**

The ancients doubtless knew how to solve a quadratic equation with numerical coefficients in the real-number system only. It is believed that Diophantus was in possession of the quadratic formula almost as we know it today, but he appears to have used only the positive sign with the radical, thereby obtaining only one root to the equation. When this root was irrational or imaginary, he rejected it as "impossible," so that he really only found solutions in the rational number system.

It was not until the sixteenth century that a formula was found which gives the three solutions of a general **cubic** (third-degree) **equation** in one unknown. This formula is more complicated than the quadratic formula and requires the finding of a cube root as well as a square root. We are told that it was first obtained by an Italian, Nicolo Fontana, called TAR-TAGLIA, who was born about 1500 A.D. and died in 1547. Tartaglia was challenged by ANTONIO DEL FIORE, who had learned from his master, SCIPIONE FERRO, a solution of the cubic equation of the form $x^3+px=r$. According to the challenge,*

* W. W. R. Ball, *A Short Account of the History of Mathematics* (London: Macmillan & Co., 1919), p. 218.

each of them was to deposit a certain stake with a notary, and whoever could solve the most problems out of a collection of thirty propounded by the other was to get the stakes, thirty days being allowed for the solution of the questions proposed.

Tartaglia was aware that his adversary was acquainted with the solution of a cubic equation of some particular form, and suspecting that the questions proposed to him would all depend on the solutions of such cubic equations, set himself the problem to find a general solution, and certainly discovered how to obtain a solution of some if not all cubic equations. His solution is believed to have depended on a geometrical construction, but led to the formula which is often, but unjustly, described as Cardan's.

Cubic equation rumpus

When the contest took place, all of the questions proposed to Tartaglia were, as he had suspected, reducible to the solution of a cubic equation, and he succeeded within two hours in bringing them to particular cases of the equation $x^3 + px = r$, of which he knew [a formula for] the solution. His opponent failed to solve any of the problems proposed to him, most of which were, as a matter of fact, reducible to numerical equations of the form $x^3 + qx^2 = r$. Tartaglia was therefore the conqueror: he subsequently composed some verses commemorative of his victory.

Instead of proudly sharing his discovery with all who might be interested, as is the custom among mathematicians today, he kept it a profound secret and gave

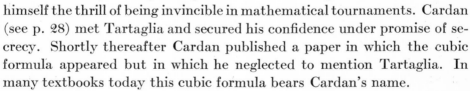

himself the thrill of being invincible in mathematical tournaments. Cardan (see p. 28) met Tartaglia and secured his confidence under promise of secrecy. Shortly thereafter Cardan published a paper in which the cubic formula appeared but in which he neglected to mention Tartaglia. In many textbooks today this cubic formula bears Cardan's name.

The discovery of more than one formula for the general **quartic** (fourth-degree) or **biquadratic equation** followed close on the heels of Cardan's paper; and many mathematicians quite naturally busied themselves seeking formulas for the general quintic, sextic, etc.—in fact, they were hopeful that a general formula could be found which, in addition to the symbols used for the coefficients of the various powers of the unknown, would also contain a symbol, say n, for the degree of the equation. They hoped that when they set $n=2$, the general formula would become the quadratic formula; that when they set $n=3$, the general formula would become the cubic formula; in fact, they sought one formula for all real polynomial equations. The search went on for almost three hundred years, in which time many mathematicians tried their hands at it with more or less diligence, but without avail.

The answer was found in 1824 by a gifted young Norwegian, NIELS HENRICK ABEL (1802–29); but it was not the answer which had been anticipated. Abel proved in a series of brilliant papers that it is not possible that there can be a formula by use of which the five solutions of

Niels Henrick Abel

a quintic, the six solutions of a sextic, ... , or the n solutions of an n-ic $(n>4)$ may be obtained by substituting numerical values of the coefficients appearing in the equation and performing the operations of arithmetic. His proof was examined with care and found to be correct.

This does not mean that quintics, sextics, etc., cannot be solved; as a matter of fact, there are *methods* for solving any given real polynomial equation; but, except for very special forms, equations of degree 5 or more must be treated separately. The solutions cannot be found *by substituting in a formula*.

The process of finding all *rational* roots of a given polynomial equation is a very simple one and is explained in any good text on college algebra in the chapter on theory of equations. In the next section is explained a method of finding *successive approximations of an irrational root* of a real equation. It may be omitted without interference with the understanding of later sections, since it is not used in the further development of the theory.

5. Approximate solutions. As examples of problems for which approximate solutions may be desired we give the following:

(1) An aviator flies due east from A to B, then due north from B to C. He notes that the distance from B to C lacks 50 mi. of being twice as far as from A to B. If the distance from A to C is 320 mi., how far is it from A to B? The answer, approximately 162.76, is a root of the equation $x^2 - 40x - 19{,}980 = 0$.

(2) The capacity of a rectangular vat whose dimensions are 4, 5, and 6 ft. is to be increased 60 cu. ft. by adding the same amount to each dimension. What should this amount be? The answer is a root of the cubic equation $x^3 + 15x^2 + 74x = 60$. It is approximately 0.705 ft.

This method for finding an approximate value of an irrational root is shown here by applying it to a quadratic equation. A person who knows the quadratic formula and knows the process of extracting the square root would use the latter processes for solving a quadratic equation. The method of approximation, however, is rather formidable because of the arithmetic and algebra needed if the degree of the equation is high. For this reason the quadratic is chosen for the first and a cubic for the second illustration.

Consider the equation

$$x^2 + 3x - 5 = 0 . \tag{1}$$

A number which is a solution of (1) will, when substituted for x, reduce the left member to zero, since the right member is zero. Let us try $x = 1$; this makes the left member -1. Try $x = 2$; the left member becomes $+5$. We suspect that there is a number between 1 and 2 which reduces the left member to zero. In fact, it is proved in the calculus that if the left member of an equation formed by setting a polynomial equal to zero has different signs (one $+$ and one $-$) for $x = a$ and $x = b$ $(a < b)$, then there is at least one root of the equation which is greater than a and less than b. We have, then, a root of our equation (1) which is greater than 1 and less than 2. Let it be denoted by $1 + h$. Then h is a *positive number smaller than unity*. Thus a *first* (rough) *approximation* of the root of the given equation is $x = 1$.

When $1 + h$ is substituted for x in the left member, since by our assumption $1 + h$ is the true value of the root, we must have

$$(1+h)^2 + 3(1+h) - 5 = 0 ,$$

or

$$h^2 + 5h - 1 = 0 . \tag{2}$$

We have now reduced the problem of finding the root of the x-equation which has a root between 1 and 2 to the problem of finding the root of an h-equation which has a root between 0 and 1.

By trial, since $h < 1$, we get

$$h = 0.1 , \qquad h^2 + 5h - 1 = -0.49 ,$$

$$h = 0.2 , \qquad h^2 + 5h - 1 = +0.04 .$$

We conclude that the true value of h lies between 0.1 and 0.2 and that a *second approximation* to x is 1.2. Since the right-hand member is nearer zero when h is 0.2 than when h is 0.1, we set $h = 0.2 - k$; then k is a positive number whose value is less than 0.1, and equation (2) becomes

$$(0.2 - k)^2 + 5(0.2 - k) - 1 = 0 ,$$

or

$$k^2 - 5.4k + 0.04 = 0 .$$

By trial, since $k < 0.1$, we get

$$k = 0.007 , \qquad k^2 - 5.4k + 0.04 = +0.002249 ,$$

$$k = 0.008 , \qquad k^2 - 5.4k + 0.04 = -0.003136 .$$

The conclusion is that the true value of k lies between 0.007 and 0.008 and that a *third approximation* to x is $1.2 - 0.007 = 1.193$.

This process may be continued until any desired degree of accuracy is obtained. The next step would be to set $k = 1.193 - t$ or $1.192 + t$ and by trial find an approximation to t.

The steps in a second example are shown next with less comment.

EXAMPLE. Find the root of $x^3 + x^2 - 12x - 1 = 0$ which lies between 3 and 4.
SOLUTION. $3^3 + 3^2 - 12(3) - 1 = -1$, $4^3 + 4^2 - 12(4) - 1 = 31$.
The *first approximation* is $x = 3$. Set $x = 3 + h$; then h is positive and less than unity.

$$(3 + h)^3 + (3 + h)^2 - 12(3 + h) - 1 = h^3 + 10h^2 + 21h - 1 = 0 .$$

By trial,

$$h = 0.04 , \qquad h^3 + 10h^2 + 21h - 1 = -0.143936 ,$$

$$h = 0.05 , \qquad h^3 + 10h^2 + 21h - 1 = +0.075125 .$$

A *second approximation* is 3.05; set $h = 0.05 - k$, then

$$(0.05 - k)^3 + 10(0.05 - k)^2 + 21(0.05 - k) - 1 =$$

$$k^3 - 10.15k^2 + 22.0075k - 0.075125 = 0 .$$

By trial,

$$k = 0.003 , \qquad k^3 - \cdots = -0.009193823 ,$$

$$k = 0.004 , \qquad k^3 - \cdots = +0.012742664 .$$

A *third approximation* is $x = 3.05 - 0.003 = 3.047$, etc.

A second example illustrating this method of approximation is given on page 183.

CHAPTER 4

GEOMETRY AND TRIGONOMETRY

THE origins of geometry are naturally unknown. The Egyptians were certainly familiar with notions of perpendicularity and of parallelism, with the conditions of equality of triangles, and with the simplest properties of a circle and of a sphere; but there are no records which date the beginnings. For us the history of geometry begins with THALES (about 600 B.C.), who is responsible for the statement that *the lengths of the sides of two triangles with equal angles are proportional.* That up to this time geometrical knowledge was hardly more than the instinctive notions which result simply from observation will be apparent presently when the methods used by Thales to obtain the height of a pyramid or obelisk are explained.

ΜΗΔΕΙΣ ΑΓΕΩΜΕΤΡΗΤΟΣ
ΕΙΣΙΤΩ ΜΟΥ ΤΗΝ ΣΤΕΓΗΝ

Plato points to motto

From the time of Thales, however, there are sufficient records to show that during the next few centuries the Egyptians discovered many of the properties of plane and spherical figures which appeared later (third century before Christ) in Euclid's *Elements*. Plato (429–348 B.C.) required geometry as a prerequisite to his philosophical lectures, and we are told that over the door of his school was the inscription "Let none ignorant of geometry enter my door."

The geometry of the Egyptians reached the Greeks in large part from the early Alexandrian school. The Greeks, in particular Plato and his followers, extended it to a *science* based on a set of assumptions—in fact, made of it a *deductive science* so perfect in construction that, as it is taught today in our schools, it is scarcely more rigorous than when Euclid collected it, organized it, and gave it to the world.

1. Some famous geometrical problems of antiquity. The experience of the mathematical world in having Abel produce a proof that an algebraical problem could not be solved by a given method after that problem had been under consideration for almost three hundred years has been paralleled by similar experiences with regard to three important geometrical problems, viz., (*a*) *trisection of an angle*, (*b*) *duplication of a cube*, (*c*) *quadrature of a circle*, called also *squaring a circle*. All three of these problems date back to antiquity; and it was only in recent times that it has been shown that it is not possible to solve them by the use of straightedge and compasses alone, i.e., by lines and circles (Euclidean geometry). In spite of proofs to the contrary, many persons are still attempting to find solutions to these problems using ruler and compasses, and it is not unusual to see a statement in the newspaper that this age-old problem has at last been solved. Such solutions are frequently excellent approximations to the result which is sought. Professor L. E. Dickson, in *Monographs on Modern Mathematics*,* shows by analytical methods that each of these problems can be reduced to that of solving a certain type of cubic equation which has no rational root. He further shows that the roots of such cubic equations cannot be constructed by use of ruler and compasses alone.

All of these problems can be solved by use of conic sections and also by use of certain other higher-plane curves.†

The problem of *duplicating a cube* is said to have originated when the oracle at Delphi was consulted in regard to a means of placating the gods who had inflicted a scourge on a tribe in ancient Greece. The oracle assured the unhappy messengers that the scourge would be abated if the golden cubical altar in the temple of Apollo were replaced by another golden cubical altar containing twice as much gold.

---

* Chap. viii. Longman's, Green. 1911.

† See Logsdon, *Elementary Mathematical Analysis* (New York: McGraw-Hill Book Co., Inc., 1933), II, 124 ff.

To *square a circle* means to find a square whose area is equal to the area of a given circle. In its first form this problem asked for a rectangle whose dimensions have the same ratio as that of the circumference of a circle to its radius. The proof of the impossibility of solving this by use of ruler and compasses alone followed immediately from the proof, in very recent times, that π cannot be the root of a polynomial equation with rational coefficients. This was the last of the three problems to be definitely settled for all time.

2. Problem of Thales. A. To measure the height of a pyramid. Thales used

two methods, each of which required no more geometry than the knowledge of the properties of similar triangles. A clever college Freshman will think that Thales does not deserve a great deal of credit for his solutions of this problem; but when one considers how little had been done at this time (600 B.C.) beyond counting and operating with objects at hand, one must realize that the accomplishment of Thales was an event of much importance.

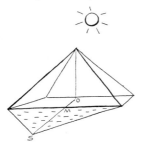

Pyramid measurement

First method. Fasten a stick upright in the ground and measure its length from the tip to the ground. Watch the shadow of the stick until the length of the shadow is exactly equal to the length of the stick. At that instant, mark the position of the end of the shadow of the pyramid. The height of the pyramid is equal to the length of the shadow, which must now be measured. This is not a particularly simple thing to do, inasmuch as it is not easy to measure accurately a line (e.g., SM in the accompanying figure) on the earth's surface, and there is also the necessity of ascertaining the length of MO where O is the center of the base. The latter computation is further complicated if the line SMO is not perpendicular to the edge of the base. Crude as this method appears, when Thales employed it and announced his result it was thought that he had done a very remarkable thing.

Second method. The first method used by Thales to measure the height of the pyramid had the disadvantage that the observations must be made at the exact moment when the elevation of the sun was 45°. If the sun were obscured by a cloud at the critical moment, the experiment must be repeated another day. Perhaps these possible inconveniences were the cause of his developing the second method, as follows: Fasten a stick upright in the ground and measure its length from tip to ground.

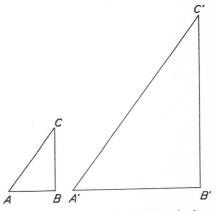

At any convenient instant mark on the ground the end of the shadow of the stick and the end of the shadow of the pyramid. Measure the lengths of the two shadows and make, as before, a calculation for the distance from the edge of the base of the pyramid to the center of the base. On a drawing board, using any convenient scale, draw two similar right triangles, ABC and $A'B'C'$, making the lengths of AB, BC, and $A'B'$ proportional, respectively, to the measured lengths of shadow of stick, stick, and shadow of pyramid. The length of $B'C'$ measured on the same scale gives the height of the pyramid.

Some of the disadvantages of the first method are overcome in the second, but there still must be taken into consideration the fact that when several lines are constructed and measurements made the cumulative error might assume surprising proportions. In the next section it will be shown that a greater degree of accuracy is possible when the solution of this problem is obtained by use of a simple trigonometrical definition.

B. To find the distance of a ship at sea. The method used by Thales to solve this problem required the measurement of an angle and one length instead of three lengths as in the previous example. Assuming that the distance of the ship from the shore is not enough to make it necessary to take into account the curvature of the earth, he probably used a procedure similar to the following:

Ship at sea

From a point A, on a tower or lighthouse, whose distance, h, above the water is known, measure the angle* BAS (cf. the figure) in a vertical plane; it is the angle between the horizontal direction at A and the direction toward the ship and is called the **angle of depression** of the ship at A. The angle MAS is equal to 90° minus the angle BAS. Draw a right triangle containing an angle equal to MAS and compute the ratio, say k, of the side opposite the angle MAS to the side adjacent. From the property of similar triangles we have

$$\frac{MS}{h} = k \; ;$$

hence,
$$MS = kh \; .$$

3. Trigonometric functions. Trigonometry grew out of the necessity or the desire to measure distances to inaccessible objects and to establish

---

* Today we have the surveyor's transit with which angles can be measured with a high degree of accuracy. A skilful surveyor uses the chain or tape little and the transit a great deal. Even with no transit at hand, a circular scale (a circle divided into equal parts) can be home made and used to measure angles with a fair degree of accuracy.

and maintain boundary lines. The word "trigonometry" comes from two Greek words meaning "triangle measuring," and in the beginning it dealt solely with computational problems involving triangles. After the invention of the calculus, however, the notions of trigonometry led to the development of trigonometrical analysis, which plays an important part in many of the practical applications of the calculus as well as in higher analysis. In this book will be considered, in the main, only some of the developments of the theory of the use of triangles by the ancients for definite practical purposes.

Attention has already been called to the fact that angles can be measured with a higher degree of accuracy than lengths on the earth's surface. In the endeavor to find methods of computing which give reasonably accurate results, it is quite logical to study the relation of a triangle to its angles, so that, in finding data to use in computation, the measurement of angles may replace, whenever possible, the measurement of lines. Until statement is made to the contrary, only right triangles will be considered.

In the accompanying figure, angle $A =$ angle A' and angle $M =$ angle M', while angle $A \neq$ angle M.* By Thales' theorem we can write out

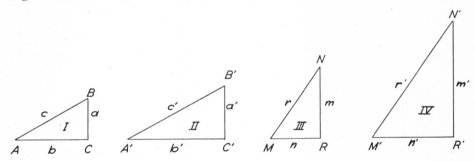

for each pair of similar triangles as many equal ratios (six in all) as there are ways of representing the quotient of one of the three symbols a, b, c by a different one of the same symbols; e.g.,

$$\frac{a}{b} = \frac{a'}{b'}, \qquad \frac{a}{c} = \frac{a'}{c'}, \qquad \frac{b}{c} = \frac{b'}{c'}, \qquad \frac{b}{a} = \frac{b'}{a'}, \qquad \frac{c}{a} = \frac{c'}{a'}, \qquad \frac{c}{b} = \frac{c'}{b'};$$

$$\frac{m}{n} = \frac{m'}{n'}, \qquad \frac{m}{r} = \frac{m'}{r'}, \qquad \text{etc.}$$

* The symbol $\neq$ means "is not equal to."

Now consider any other right triangle containing an angle equal to angle A of triangle I. Whether the length of the opposite side a is 1 in., 1 ft., or 10,000 mi., *the ratio of the opposite side to the adjacent side* is equal to the same number a/b as is obtained from triangle I. Moreover, since angle $M \neq$ angle A, we see at once that the number m/n is not equal to the number a/b.

Let the angle A be thought of as increasing gradually until it becomes almost as large as a right angle (since angle A is an acute angle in a right triangle, it cannot become equal to 90° but it can become as near to 90° in value as we wish), let the leg opposite A be denoted always by a, and the leg adjacent to A by b, while the hypotenuse will be denoted by c. Then, as A increases, so does the ratio a/b; whereas, if A decreases, so does the ratio a/b. When A is almost 90°, a/b is very large; when A is little larger than zero, a/b is very small. *The number a/b depends on the angle A and depends* **only** *on the angle A.*

In mathematics, as in the world about us, when one quantity depends on a second quantity, or when the value of one symbol depends on the value of another symbol, the first is said to be a **function** of the second. If the second quantity, or the second symbol, is thought of as taking on a number of arbitrary values (e.g., the angle A when it increases or decreases), it is called an **independent variable** and the function which depends on it is called a **dependent variable**. It may happen that a function depends on more than one independent variable.

EXAMPLES.

a) The surface of a sphere is a function of its radius. This function can be given by a mathematical formula, viz., $S = 4\pi r^2$.

b) The cost of mailing a parcel-post package is a function of its weight and of the zone to which it is directed.

c) The cost of my winter coal is a function of a number of things, among which are the quality of the coal, the size of the house to be heated, the climate in that location, the distance from a mining center, and general labor conditions.

d) If $y = x^2$, y is a (quadratic) function of x.

e) Another function of x is given by $y = 3x - 2$. This is a *linear function* of x.

f) Force is a function of both mass and acceleration. This function can be expressed by a mathematical formula, viz., $F = ma$.

g) The distance which a freely falling body, starting at rest, falls is a function of the time which has elapsed since the body started falling. The formula is $s = \frac{1}{2}gt^2$.

h) The equation $5x+2y-6=0$ *defines y as a function of x*, viz., $y=-\frac{5}{2}x+3$. The equation also *defines x as a function of y*, viz., $x=-\frac{2}{5}y+\frac{6}{5}$. When there is a relationship between two variables, either one can be looked upon as the independent variable, since for an arbitrary value given to one variable the known relationship shows that there is one or more corresponding values for the other. It is customary, when x and y are the symbols used for the two variables, to let the independent variable be denoted by x and the dependent variable by y.

i) In a right triangle the ratio of the leg opposite an acute angle to the leg adjacent to that angle is a function of the (size of the) angle.

It is convenient to give a name to the last-mentioned function. We say the **tangent** of the angle A is equal to a/b where A, a, and b are parts of a triangle related as described above. In writing, the definition of the tangent of the angle A is abbreviated to merely

$$\tan A = \frac{a}{b} \qquad \left(\text{or, } \tan A = \frac{\text{opposite leg}}{\text{adjacent leg}} \right),$$

which is read "tangent $A = a/b$."

In the same way, the ratios a/c, b/c, etc., of the sides of a right triangle are functions of the angles; and, for convenience, names are given to them. The ratio a/c is called the **sine** of the angle A; the ratio b/c is called the **cosine** of the angle A; etc. In this chapter we shall discuss more in detail some of the uses of the tangent function, the one which proves to be of service in computing the value of the third symbol when two of the three symbols A, a, and b are known. The reader will see that in similar manner the sine and cosine functions are of service in computing the value of the third when two of the three symbols A, a, and c or A, b, and c are known.

Similarly, we can write out the functions of the angle B which is also an acute angle in a right triangle:*

$$\tan B = \frac{b}{a}, \qquad \sin B = \frac{b}{c}, \qquad \cos B = \frac{a}{c}.$$

---

* Since we are discussing only the beginnings of trigonometry, our definitions of trigonometric functions are given for *acute* angles only. Modern trigonometry defines the functions in a more general way—in fact, formulates definitions in such a manner that we can speak of the trigonometric functions of angles of any magnitude whatever.

4. How to compute tangents. From the definition of tan A it is possible to obtain an approximate value of the tangent of any given angle by use of a protractor, a pair of compasses, and a graduated scale, or merely a protractor and a sheet of *squared paper* (called also *graph paper* and *coordinate paper*). For example, suppose it is desired to compute tan $27°$. On a straight line mark off a point A, which is to be the vertex of the angle. (See the figure.) With the protractor draw from A a line making an

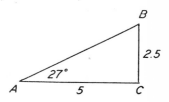

angle of $27°$ with the first line. Use the scale to find the position of the point C so that AC has any convenient length. Since presently it will be necessary to divide by the length of AC, it is convenient to take AC equal to 5 cm. or 10 cm. or 2 in. At C erect a perpendicular cutting the oblique line at B. This perpendicular can be constructed quite accurately with ruler and compasses; or, if squared paper is used, it is already printed on the sheet. Now measure the line segment CB and divide its length by the length of AC. The quotient is tan $27°$. If the construction has been made carefully, the result should be $\frac{1}{2}$ or, perhaps, 0.51.

In the same manner it is possible to compute the value of the tangent of any given angle correct to two decimal places.

The reader should practice on this construction until he is sure that he understands it and can get good results. The following list of tangents will be needed in later pages:

tan $\ 5° = 0.087$	tan $50° = \ 1.192$
tan $10° = 0.176$	tan $55° = \ 1.428$
tan $15° = 0.268$	tan $60° = \ 1.732$
tan $20° = 0.364$	tan $65° = \ 2.145$
tan $25° = 0.466$	tan $70° = \ 2.747$
tan $30° = 0.577$	tan $75° = \ 3.732$
tan $35° = 0.700$	tan $80° = \ 5.671$
tan $40° = 0.839$	tan $85° = 11.430$
tan $45° = 1.000$	

In problems concerned with triangles, a value of a tangent which is correct to two decimal places only does not give very accurate results; hence there is needed a more refined determination of tangents than can be obtained by drawing and measuring lines. The calculus supplies a formula by use of which the value of the tangent of any given angle may be computed correct to as many decimal places as desired. The necessary computations have been made and checked many times and the results collected in **tables of tangents**. In the foregoing table there are entries for all angles between 0° and 90° which are multiples of 5; other tables have entries for every degree; still others have entries for every minute, for every 10 sec., etc.

From now on, when a tangent is needed, we can look it up in a table of tangents.

5. Some uses of the tangent in solving triangles. Before we attempt to use the tangent in finding the unknown parts of a right triangle, let us see how much algebra is needed for this problem. In the first place, a right triangle is determined if two of the three sides or a side and an acute angle are given. Each definition of a trigonometric function contains three symbols, two of which are lengths of sides and the third an acute angle. Thus, if values are known for two of these symbols, one and only one value can be computed for the third; the three numbers associated in this way are parts of a right triangle. For example, from the three equations

$$\tan A = \frac{a}{b}, \qquad \sin A = \frac{a}{c}, \qquad \cos A = \frac{b}{c},$$

we can formulate and solve the following nine types of problems:

Given	Find	Solution
1) a, b	A	$\tan A = a/b$, take A from a table of tangents
2) b, A	a	$a = b \tan A$, where $\tan A$ is taken from a table
3 a, A	b	$b = a/\tan A$
4) a, c	A	$\sin A = a/c$, take A from a table of sines
5) c, A	a	$a = c \sin A$, where $\sin A$ is taken from a table
6) a, A	c	$c = a/\sin A$
7) b, c	A	$\cos A = b/c$, take A from a table of cosines
8) c, A	b	$b = c \cos A$, where $\cos A$ is taken from a table
9) b, A	c	$c = b/\cos A$

The second problem of Thales (cf. p. 63) can now be solved more readily and more correctly than was possible before. We take the tangent of the angle MAS from a table of tangents and multiply it by h.

$$MS = h \tan MAS .$$

A second illustrative problem is the following: When standing 100 ft. from the base of a tree, John found that the angle of elevation of the top of the tree was 35°. Find the height, h, of the tree. You can draw your own figure for this problem. The angle of elevation is the angle between the horizontal line from John's eye to the tree and the oblique line from his eye to the top of the tree.

SOLUTION. $h = 100 \tan 35° = 70$ ft. Hence the height of the tree is 70 ft. plus John's height.

Another illustration of the use of the tangent is found in a story told of Napoleon. With his army he once came to the bank of a swollen stream and found that the bridge had been washed away. It was necessary to build a bridge at once, and of course it was important to know the approximate span. Napoleon called for someone who could compute the width of the stream. Finally a private was found who volunteered to solve the problem. This is his method: Line up two trees, T_1 on the near bank and T_2 on the far bank, so that the direction T_1T_2 is perpendicular to the river bank. Lay off T_1A, any convenient length on the near

Napoleon's bridge

side, so that AT_1 is perpendicular at T_1 to the direction T_1T_2. Measure AT_1 and measure the angle T_1AT_2. Then $T_1T_2 = AT_1 \tan A$.

It is said that the bridge was soon completed, that the army crossed safely, and that Napoleon rewarded the private properly.

Following is a list of problems, each of which can be solved very simply by use of the tangent function. Use the table of tangents in section 4, as needed.

1. If an aeroplane is rising at a 20° angle, how much is its elevation increased when it has gone a mile in horizontal distance?

2. A man attempts to row across a stream at 3 mi. per hr., but the stream is moving at the same rate. What angle is the man making with the bank of the stream?

3. A man builds a triangular cupboard in a corner of his house. Upon measurement, he finds its length along one wall is 1.2 times its length along the other. What angle (approximately) does the front of the cupboard make with each wall?

4. Two boys find the direct distance between a point A and a point B, due north of A, by first observing that the angle made by AC and BC, where C is a point 100 yd. east of A, is 55°. How do they compute the distance AB?

6. Vectors. In all that precedes this paragraph, when points and lengths on a line are used to represent physical and geometrical concepts it is unimportant *what* line is used, i.e., the line may be drawn in any convenient direction. We come now to a representation of certain physical concepts by line segments where the direction of the line segment is of much importance. The following two examples make plain the added information conveyed by the geometrical picture when *direction* is noted.

EXAMPLE 1. A ship sails in a straight course for 3 hr. at the rate of 10 mi. per hr., then continues in a different direction for 2 hr., at the rate of 15 mi. per hr. What is the total distance sailed?

EXAMPLE 2. A ship sails east for 3 hr. at the rate of 10 mi. per hr., then continues north for 2 hr. at the rate of 15 mi. per hr. Where is the ship at the end of the 5 hr.?

The first example is answered geometrically by any one of the broken lines $A_1B_1C_1$, $A_2B_2C_2$, etc., in the figure and also by $C_1B_1A_1$, $C_2B_2A_2$, etc.

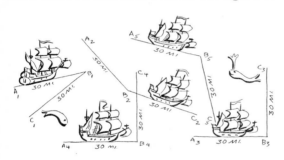

The second example is answered geometrically by $A_3B_3C_3$ and by $A_4B_4C_4$ and by no others of the broken lines in the figure. Arithmetically, the answer to the first question is *60 mi.*, while the answer to the second one is $30\sqrt{2}$ *mi. northeast of the starting-point.*

Imagine two planes which at a given instant are traveling due west at the rate of 120 mi. per hr. At this instant one plane may be over Chicago and the other over Denver. To represent the motion of each of these planes correctly by means of a line segment, the cardinal directions must be indicated and the line segment must be drawn so as to show motion toward the west.

Again, to say that John is driving at the rate of 50 mi. per hr., is telling only half of the story, but to say that John is driving north at the rate of 50 mi. per hr. gives a complete description of his motion.

Thus, a number alone cannot completely describe velocity; there must also be given a direction and a sense. For this reason, velocity is called a **vector quantity**. Another well-known vector quantity is force.

The result of the action of a force whose magnitude is known cannot be determined until we know the direction in which the force acts.

When we define a **vector** as any straight line (e.g., M_1M_2 in the figure) which has a *definite length* and is drawn in a *definite direction* and in a *definite sense*, we are merely wishing to emphasize that the direction and the sense are both needed to complete the representation of the information at hand. The line segments in the figure have the same direction, but the sense K_1K_2 is the opposite of the sense K_2K_1. The word *vector* is the Latin word for *car-*

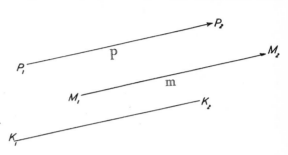

rier; and it was defined in this way in 1846 by the eminent Scottish mathematician, Sir William Rowan Hamilton, who desired to convey the idea that he was looking upon a vector as an operator which carries a particle from the **initial point** M_1 to the **terminal point** M_2. In figures, it is customary to indicate the sense in which the vector is drawn by an arrow; in the text we may write the arrow as a superscript, as $\overrightarrow{M_1M_2}$; or we may merely say vector M_1M_2, understanding thereby that M_1 is the initial point; or we may use an open-faced letter as m in the figure to designate a vector referred to in a figure. Thus we distinguish between $\overrightarrow{M_1M_2}$ and $\overrightarrow{M_2M_1}$; in the latter M_2 is the initial position of the particle and M_1 its final position. These two vectors have the same length and the same direction but opposite senses. One is called the *negative* of the other.

The vector P_1P_2 in the figure has the same length, direction, and sense as the vector M_1M_2: they differ in the position of their initial points. They are equal by the definition of equal vectors.

Definition. Two **vectors** are **equal** if they have the same length, direction, and sense.

The area of a triangle, the volume of a vessel, the distance from Washington to Boston, the length of a line segment—each of these quantities is described by a number only. There is no expressed or implied notion of direction. Such quantities are called **scalars.** *The length of a vector is a scalar.* When we use as vector symbols a, b, c, etc., their lengths will be denoted by *a*, *b*, *c*, etc. Similarly, the vector symbol v will designate velocity, while speed will be given by *v*.

   7. Vector addition.* A vector c, called the sum of vector a and vector b,

$$c = a + b \, ,$$

is obtained geometrically in either of the two following ways: Place the *initial* point of b on the *terminal* point of a; the sum vector extends *from the initial point of a to the terminal point of b.* Or, place the *initial* point of a on the *terminal* point of b; the sum vector extends *from the initial point of b to the terminal point of a.* The two vectors thus obtained are equal (see the figure) since they have the same magnitude, the same direction, and the same sense.

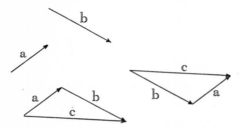

   If two given vectors a and b have the same direction and the same sense, the length of the sum vector is equal to the sum of the lengths of the two given vectors (this is the only case in the addition of vectors where the geometric sum is equal to the arithmetic sum); if the given vectors have the same direction and opposite senses, the length of the sum vector is the difference of the lengths of the two given vectors; if the two given vectors do not have the same direction, it is evident that the sum vector is the third side of a triangle of which the two *components* a and b are sides and that also the sum vector is a diagonal of a parallelogram of which the given vectors a and b are adjacent sides. For this reason vector addition is said to obey the **parallelogram law.**

   When the given vectors do not have the same direction, let the angle between them be denoted by θ. We wish to determine the length *c* of the vector c and also the direction of c. To find the direction of c we may find the angle which c makes with a or with b.

   * See Harvey Brace Lemon, *From Galileo to Cosmic Rays* (Chicago: University of Chicago Press, 1934), p. 40, and Reginald J. Stephenson, *Exploring in Physics* (Chicago: University of Chicago Press, 1935), chap. 3.

To solve this problem we must make use of two formulas in trigonometry which have not yet been proved but whose proofs are simple. They are the Law of Sines and the Law of Cosines. At this point these laws will be stated only, but proofs are given in Appendix B on pages 177–78.

Law of Sines. *In any triangle, two sides have the same ratio as the sines of the angles opposite these sides.*

Law of Cosines. *In any triangle, the square of a side is equal to the sum of the squares of the other two sides diminished by twice the product of these sides by the cosine of the included angle.*

In symbols, the respective laws are written

$$\frac{a}{b} = \frac{\sin A}{\sin B}, \qquad c^2 = a^2 + b^2 - 2ab \cos C.$$

If now we have given two vectors, we draw two equal vectors from the same initial point, O in the figure, and call the angle between them θ. Complete the parallelogram and label the angle θ', as in the figure. By elementary geometry

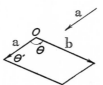
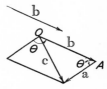

$$\theta + \theta' = 180°$$

and the angles θ and θ' are called *supplementary*. Draw the diagonal c, the sum of the two vectors. Then in both of the triangles which have the vectors a, b, and c as sides the angle included between vectors a and b is θ'. By the Law of Cosines the length of vector c is given by the formula

$$c^2 = a^2 + b^2 - 2ab \cos \theta'.$$

Note. Before the last formula can be used for an arbitrary pair of vectors, a remark about cos θ' is needed. When the cosine of an angle was defined on page 66, the definition was given for acute angles in right triangles. If θ is greater than 90°, as in the figure, θ' is less than 90°; hence a right triangle may be drawn containing θ' as one acute angle and the cosine of θ' estimated by measurement, or it may be looked up in a table of cosines. However, if θ is less than 90°, θ' is greater than 90° and a definition of cos θ' is necessary before the formula can be used. In trigonometry texts the trigonometric functions are defined for angles of any magnitude whatever, but obviously an arbitrary angle cannot be a part of a right triangle and hence the definitions cannot be in terms of opposite side, adjacent side, and hypotenuse. Without giving the definitions for the general case* here, we merely

---

* See Logsdon, *op. cit.*, I, 32, problem 4, for the two formulas in the Note, and pages 22 and 31 for definitions of the cosine and the sine of a general angle.

say that, according to these definitions, if $\theta+\theta'=180°$, it is always true that $\cos\theta=-\cos\theta'$ and, obviously, $\cos\theta'=-\cos\theta$. Hence, if θ' is greater than 90° (in which case its cosine is not given in a table of cosines, nor can it be computed by our definition of a cosine), we use the table of cosines to ascertain $\cos\theta$ and then use the negative of this number in the formula. In case the sine of an angle greater than 90° is needed, we use the relation $\sin A=\sin B$ if $A+B=180°$.

EXAMPLE. Vector a is 10 in. in length and is directed toward the right on a horizontal line; vector b is 16 in. in length and is directed from left to right on a line which makes an angle of 60° with the horizontal. Find the length and direction of the sum of the two vectors.

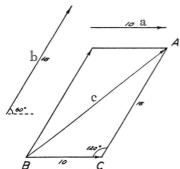

Solution. Let the sum vector be denoted by c. Then, since $\theta=60°$, we have $\theta'=120°$, and

$$c^2=10^2+16^2-2(10)(16)\cos 120°$$
$$=100+256-320(-\cos 60°)$$
$$=356+320\cos 60°$$
$$=356+320(\tfrac{1}{2})$$
$$=356+160=512\;.$$
$$c=\sqrt{512}=\sqrt{2(256)}=16\sqrt{2}\;.$$

To find the direction of c we use the Law of Sines, as follows:

$$\frac{AC}{BA}=\frac{\sin ABC}{\sin BCA}\,,\qquad \frac{16}{16\sqrt{2}}=\frac{\sin ABC}{\sin 120°}=\frac{\sin ABC}{\sin 60°}=\frac{\sin ABC}{\tfrac{1}{2}\sqrt{3}}\;.$$

This gives

$$\sin ABC=\frac{\sqrt{3}}{2\sqrt{2}}\;.$$

When an approximate value of this fraction is computed in decimals, the value of the angle CAB can be found by use of a table of sines.

8. Resultant of two forces. A certain force F can move a given object from A to B; a second force f can move the object from A to C. If the two forces act in succession, the object moves from A to B to D, or else from A to C to D (cf. the figure).

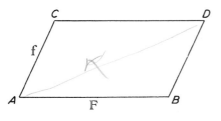

There is a force R which is capable of moving the object from A to D along the straight line AD, that is, *a single force* which accomplishes the same result as that accomplished by the two forces acting separately. This force R is called the **resultant** of the forces F and f, and the two forces

F and f are called **components** of R. Just as AD can be the diagonal of many parallelograms, so R can have many pairs of components.

Experience in and out of the laboratory has led to the conclusion that if F and f act *simultaneously* on an object at A which is free to move, the path taken will be along AD (the vector AD is the sum of the two vectors AB and AC) to D. In other words, when the vectors represent forces, the vector sum is the resultant of the two forces.

Hence, *to find the magnitude of the resultant of two forces, we use the Law of Cosines, while to find its direction, we use the Law of Sines.*

EXAMPLE 1. A force of 18 lb. is resolved into two components which make angles of 10° and 20°, respectively, with the direction of the given force. Find the component forces.

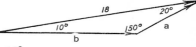

SOLUTION. From the Law of Sines, we have

$$\frac{a}{18}=\frac{\sin 10°}{\sin 150°}=\frac{\sin 10°}{\sin 30°},$$

$$\frac{b}{18}=\frac{\sin 20°}{\sin 150°}=\frac{\sin 20°}{\sin 30°}.$$

Hence,

$$a=\frac{18\sin 10°}{\frac{1}{2}}=36\sin 10°=36(0.174)=6.264,$$

$$b=\frac{18\sin 20°}{\frac{1}{2}}=36\sin 20°=36(0.342)=12.312.$$

EXAMPLE 2. A man can row in still water at the rate of 4 mi. per hr. He wishes to cross a stream whose rate is 3 mi. per hr. The width of the stream is $\frac{3}{4}$ mi. If he heads his boat straight across, where will he land?

SOLUTION. The left-hand drawing in the figure shows the vector AD, which represents the rate of the stream, and the vector AC, which represents the rate of the rower.

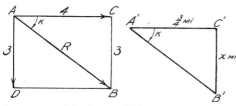

The sum vector AB (the resultant) makes an angle K, whose tangent is $\frac{3}{4}$, with the direction straight across the river. The second drawing shows the line across the river, $\frac{3}{4}$ mi., represented by $A'C'$ and the path of the boat by $A'B'$, which makes an angle equal to K with the direction across the stream. The boat will land at B', whose distance from C' is computed as follows:

$$C'B'=\frac{3}{4}\tan K=\frac{3}{4}\cdot\frac{3}{4}=\frac{9}{16}.$$

Hence the boat lands at a point 9/16 mi. downstream from the point directly across from its starting-point.

Consider, now, an object which is acted upon simultaneously by three forces whose magnitudes and directions are given by the vectors $\overrightarrow{OA}$, $\overrightarrow{OB}$, and $\overrightarrow{OC}$ in the drawing. We add b to a and then add c to the sum of a and b

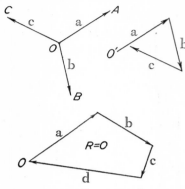

by placing the initial point of c on the terminal point of a+b. Then R, the sum of the three vectors, has its initial point at the initial point of a and its terminal point at the terminal point of c. In the figure it is seen that, if R were drawn, it would be very small. If it happens that the triangle of vectors closes, there is no motion of the object at O, since R = 0. In this case c = −(a+b); also b = −(a+c) and a = −(b+c). Similarly, when four or more vectors are added, *if they form a closed polygon their resultant is zero* and any one of the vectors is the negative of the sum of the remaining vectors.

The subject of vectors will be referred to again in section 6 of the next chapter.

9. Some trigonometrical problems of antiquity. As soon as their civilization reached the stage of individual ownership of land, the Egyptians were faced with the necessity of finding a solution to an important practical problem. The annual inundation of the Nile left in the wake of the receding waters a fertile valley capable of producing food and grain almost without limit, but with land boundaries destroyed. It was imperative to devise a method of re-establishing these boundaries so that each landowner could have exactly what belonged to him. Because demonstrative geometry was inadequate, the elements of trigonometry were developed. With this knowledge, accurate land maps could be made (see the method of triangulation in sec. 10) and lost boundaries could be regained. There are maps extant, representing small areas, which come to us from Egypt, and others from Babylonia, dating back as far as 3800 B.C.

HIPPARCHUS (second century before Christ) was the *first systematic astronomer* on record. He discovered the precession of the equinoxes and the eccentricity of the sun's path. He invented the **planisphere,** a map of the celestial sphere on a plane so constructed as to show the constellations visible at any time. It is a very remarkable fact that, with no telescope, he drew up a catalogue of 1,080 stars, recording their locations with a very high degree of accuracy, as was ascertained when their positions were re-determined by use of refined modern instruments. To carry on these re-searches, Hipparchus needed and discovered many of the properties of triangles on a plane and on a sphere which today form a considerable por-tion of the subject matter of plane and spherical trigonometry. One of his feats which wins our warm admiration was the computation of the dis-tance from the earth to the moon.

10. Some modern uses of trigonometry. In the early days of the life of our nation, an important commercial activity was shipping off the coast of New England, a rough and rugged coast with many dangerous rocks and shoals. It was important to have an accurate map of this region, a region where it is not possible to measure distances from point to point with sufficient precision to justify constructing a map based on such measurements. The U.S. Coast and Geodetic Survey was established, and to it was assigned the task of solving the problem. A highly satisfac-tory solution was found as follows. A small reasonably level tract of land of New Hampshire was selected, and on it was laid off and measured *one* length, called the **base line.** To secure as great accuracy as possible, the measuring tape was carried to Washington and compared with the stand-ard measure which is kept in the Bureau of Weights and Measures. When the tape was used in New Hampshire, a suitable correction for difference of temperature was made.

With the length of the base line ascertained, *it was never necessary to measure another line;* but by measuring suitable angles, the **method of triangulation** sufficed to construct a map ex-tending as far from the base line as desired. The method consists in computing the un-known parts of a succession of triangles, us-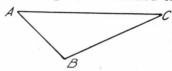
ing a computed side of one triangle as the known side of the next one. For example, let *AB* in the figure be the measured base line and let it be desired to extend a map from *AB* until it contains the point *P*, which

may be an inaccessible point on a small island or a high cliff not visible from both A and B. Choose an accessible point C visible from both A and B and measure the angles CBA and BAC. By the theory of oblique triangles, which is not explained in this book, the lengths of BC and AC can be computed.

   Note. It is evident that there is only one triangle with the given side and the two angles, since from Euclid we learn that *two triangles having a side and the two adjacent angles of the one equal, respectively, to a side and the two adjacent angles of the other are congruent.* This is another way of saying that a triangle is completely, i.e., uniquely, determined if a side and the two adjacent angles are known.

   The next step is to choose an accessible point D visible from A and from C, and measure the angles DAC and ACD. The lengths of AD and CD can now be computed. Continue with the series of triangles as long as necessary; the final step requires that the inaccessible point P shall be visible from two of the points whose distance apart has been computed in an earlier triangle.

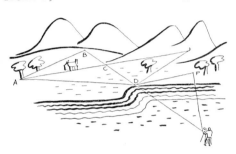

Measurement by triangulation

   The surveyor's transit, the instrument used in measuring the angles, has been set up at A, B, C, D, etc. While at these places, angle bearings of other landmarks may be taken and used to compute triangles within triangles. Thus, as many objects may be located with precision as is deemed desirable. The data obtained may now be used in constructing the required map.

   The U.S. Coast and Geodetic Survey has been in continuous existence since its first appointment and to it was subsequently assigned the task of mapping all the shore line of the United States and its possessions. This is, in truth, a stupendous commission, for, if you were to travel over all the shore line of the United States and its possessions, you would cover a distance greater than four times the circumference of the earth at the equator, viz., more than 103,000 mi. in all. In the year 1934, 21 new charts and 152 revisions of existing charts were issued by the Survey. The total number of nautical charts now issued (January, 1935) by the

Survey is 752, and these are supplemented by 5,515 coast and intra-coastal pilots, 31,609 tide and current tables, and 958 tidal current charts.

In recent years the Survey inaugurated the custom of measuring one base line in each state as a check on the computations from the original base line. Also, in more recent times the use of the radio makes it possible to perform the observational part of the work with more ease and celerity than without it. In this work, curvature of the earth must be considered; consequently, the trigonometry used is spherical trigonometry.

One of the most important scientific experiments of the last twenty years depended on the method of triangulation. This was the famous experiment made by the late PROFESSOR A. A. MICHELSON, of the University of Chicago, in determining the velocity of light. Stations were established and equipped with all necessary apparatus on the tops of two mountains in California. By a system of revolving mirrors, the time used by a ray of light in passing from one mountain to the other and back to the starting-point could be ascertained with a known very small error. The distance between the two points, found by triangulation, was more than 35,000 meters. To determine this distance three new base-line measurements were made. The accuracy is believed to be between 1 part in 500,000 and 1 part in 1,000,000, i.e., an error of not more than 6 cm. and not less than 3 cm. in this distance of almost 40 mi.

A complete account of the measurement of this distance is given in an article published in the *Astrophysical Journal*, LXV (1927), 14, written by Wm. Bowie, chief, Division of Geodesy.

CHAPTER 5

ANALYTICAL GEOMETRY

UNTIL the seventeenth century, following the pattern of Euclid, geometrical proofs were wholly synthetic. The studies and published memoirs of RENÈ DESCARTES (1596–1650), noted philosopher as well as mathematician, resulted in the introduction of a new technique, a new method of attacking geometrical problems called a **method of analysis** or **analytical geometry**. This method consists in linking algebra and geometry by means of a coordinate system which associates numbers with points. In this way the roots of an equation in one variable, being finite in number, are associated with an equal number of points on a line; while the solutions of an equation in two variables, i.e., an indeterminate equation, are associated with the infinite number of points on a curve, etc.

It was reasonable to expect that a new algebraic or analytical point of view and method of attack would lead to solutions of problems which had not hitherto yielded to synthetic treatment. This is precisely what happened. Descartes and his followers succeeded in completing proofs of theorems and in solving problems which had long been engaging their attention to no avail; they also took delight in finding new analytical proofs for problems long since completely solved by synthetic methods. Today, when a mathematician seeks to develop new theorems or new proofs, he has his choice of the synthetic or the analytical method or a combination of the two. The nature of the problem determines which method gives a simple and elegant proof.

1. **Coordinate systems. Latitude and longitude.** The purpose of a co-ordinate system is twofold. It enables one person to describe the position of points or objects in such a manner that others listening or reading may know exactly what points or objects are meant. And it is a device for linking algebra and geometry so that an algebraic equation corresponds to a geometric locus and, conversely, a geometric locus corresponds to one or more algebraic equations.

The reader is already familiar with the coordinate system, due to Hipparchus, which is used to locate points on the surface of the earth, viz., the *latitude-longitude system.* The statement, "The latitude and longitude of Chicago are roughly N. 42° and W. 88°, respectively," has meaning only when it is clearly understood that latitude is measured in degrees on a meridian north or south from the equator and that longitude is measured in degrees on the equator (or a circle parallel to it) east and west of the meridian passing through Greenwich, England (the *prime meridian*).

A coordinate system on a surface, plane or spherical, may have the same fundamental structure as the latitude-longitude system, i.e., two reference circles or lines on each of which a **linear scale** (in these cases a scale for measuring lengths) has been agreed upon. In the latitude-longi-tude system the reference lines are the equator and the prime meridian, a circle and a half-circle, respectively. On both of these scales the unit of measure is a degree of arc; but in other systems it is frequently convenient, and often necessary, to have different units of measure on the two refer-ence lines. After the frame of reference has been agreed upon, a point is located by its *distances and directions from the reference lines.* In the lati-tude-longitude system any real number from 0 to 90 can be the latitude or **first coordinate** of a given point and any real number from 0 to 180 can be the longitude or **second coordinate,** provided that with each of these numbers is used a means of designating the *direction* of the point from the reference line. On the earth's surface it is customary to designate directions by the points of the compass; but on surfaces and planes which are not thought of as oriented with respect to the cardinal points, directions are customarily distinguished by plus and minus, thus making of the distance a **signed number.** The various coordinate systems used to locate stars and other objects in the sky are similar in structure to the latitude-longitude system.*

2. **The Cartesian coordinate system in a plane.** Let us now construct a frame of reference on a plane, thereby setting up a coordinate system by means of which points of the plane shall be located in such a way that we can talk about them and understand each other. Obviously, we cannot use the geographical terms "equator," "longitude," etc., but must coin corresponding terminology. The only purpose of this is economy of words and of writing, i.e., ease of expression and clarity of thinking. For example, it is simpler to use the word "longitude" than to say "the distance from the meridian through Greenwich measured in degrees on the equator." All of the terms needed will now be defined.

Corresponding to the two reference lines on the sphere, the equator and the prime meridian, are two reference lines in the plane called **x-axis** and **y-axis,** the two together constituting the **coordinate axes.**

Corresponding to the latitude and longitude on the sphere are used the words **abscissa,** *directed distance from the* y*-axis measured on the* x*-scale,* and **ordinate,** *directed distance from the* x*-axis measured on the* y*-scale.*

In order to measure a directed distance on a line, it is necessary to establish a scale and a direction on the line. This is done by choosing *two arbitrary points* on the line and labeling them with *two arbitrary numbers.* For example, on the line in the figure, let the points A and B be labeled 2 and 4, respectively. Then the point C, which is halfway between A and B, should bear the label 3 and we have $AC = CB = 1$. Thus the length

of AC is the **unit of measure,** and with this unit we can mark off on the line the points which should be associated with the positive integers 5, 6, 7, etc., as well as 1, 0, −1, etc. In going from A toward B, motion is in the direction of *increasing* number-labels. For this reason the line segment AB is called a **positive line segment,** the direction from left to right is called the **positive direction on the line,** and the segment BA is said to

* See Walter Bartky, *Highlights of Astronomy* (Chicago: University of Chicago Press, 1935), chap. 3.

be a **negative line segment.** With other points labeled as in the figure, we say that the distance from A to M is -3 units, from O to D is 7 units, and from D to B is -3 units. The same idea is intended to be conveyed by the statement, *The length of* AM *is* -3. This indicates that line segments on this line are being thought of as **directed line segments.** The length of the line segment from the point A, labeled with the number a, to the point B, labeled with the number b, is $b-a$, while the length of BA is $a-b$ units.

We now have set up on the line an arithmetical scale on which various physical notions may have geometrical associations. Let the unit be assumed to be 1 mi. and think of John who makes a journey which corresponds to the line segment MB while Tom's journey corresponds to the segment DA. We see at once that each walks 5 mi. and that they go in opposite directions, starting at different points and ending at different points. Again, let the unit be assumed to be 10° Fahrenheit. Then the point B represents a temperature of 40° while the point M represents a temperature of $-10°$; the difference between the two readings is 50°.

Examples of linear scales are the yard stick, the meter stick, all kinds of thermometers, etc.

In setting up a linear scale on the line in the last figure, it may be more convenient to give to the points A and B, respectively, other labels. Let all of the points M, O, A, C, B, and D be marked off on the line exactly as before as regards their relative positions, but this time let the point A be associated with the number -2 and the point B with the number -10. The remaining points must now have the labels shown in the next figure. On this scale the point which corresponds to zero lies midway be-

tween the two number-labels $+2$ and -2 and the unit is one-fourth as long as the unit on the first scale. The positive direction on this line is the direction from *right to left*, instead of from left to right as before; the distance from D to B is $-10-(-22)=+12$, while that from O to A is $-2-6=-8$.

Whether the one or the other of the two scales is used, there is

    a) A single point which corresponds to a given positive or negative integer;

b) A single point which corresponds to a given positive or negative rational fraction (e.g., the point corresponding to $-8\frac{1}{2}$ lies halfway between the points which correspond respectively to -8 and -9); and

c) A single point which corresponds to a given irrational number (e.g., the point corresponding to $\sqrt{2}$ lies between the points corresponding to 1.4 and 1.5; more precisely, it lies between the points corresponding to 1.414 and 1.415).

These points can be located, when desired, with ruler and compasses with sufficient accuracy for any of the purposes for which a geometric scale is to be used. Conversely, it is assumed that a given point corresponds to one and only one real number.

On either line can be located the points which are associated with the two roots of the quadratic equation $x^2 - 6x = 0$, for example; if we choose, we can say the two points thus found are to be thought of as associated with the quadratic equation. Thus, every quadratic equation which has two real roots is associated with two points on the line; every cubic equation which has three real roots is associated with a set of three points on the line; etc.

It is customary to choose the direction *from left to right* as the positive direction on a horizontal line unless for a special problem it is more convenient to do otherwise. Let us agree, moreover, that in a given problem or discussion *the same scale and direction will be used on all horizontal lines.*

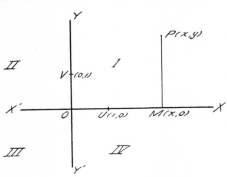

To construct a so-called **Cartesian frame of reference** for a plane, two linear scales are needed; and, as in the latitude-longitude system, it is found convenient to choose as coordinate axes two perpendicular lines.*

Denote the intersection of the two axes by the letter O and choose O as the *zero point on both scales.* If the axes are not already horizontal and

---

* When the two reference lines are perpendicular, the system is called a *rectangular* Cartesian coordinate system; when not perpendicular, it is an *oblique* Cartesian coordinate system.

vertical, turn them until they assume the directions in the figure. The horizontal line $X'OX$ is to be the **x-axis**; on it an arbitrary point U lying *to the right of O* is chosen as the **unit point** on this scale. The vertical line $Y'OY$ is the **y-axis**; on it a point V lying *above O* is chosen as the **unit point** of the y-scale. This choice fixes the *upward direction* of the y-axis as the *positive direction*.

Take an arbitrary point P in the plane and let fall a perpendicular PM from P to the x-axis. The **abscissa of P** is the directed length of OM (measured in terms of OU), and the **ordinate of P** is the directed length of MP (measured in terms of OV). When the abscissa and ordinate are not known, they are denoted by x and y, respectively. The following statements, some of which are definitions and others are observations, require no argument.

   a) The coordinate axes divide the plane into four parts called **quadrants**. The quadrants are numbered I, II, III, IV, as in the figure.

   b) The abscissa of a point is positive, negative, or zero according as the point lies to the right of, to the left of, or *on $Y'OY$*.

   c) The ordinate of a point is positive, negative, or zero according as the point lies above, below, or *on $X'OX$*.

   d) Corresponding to a given abscissa and ordinate (both real numbers), there is one and only one point in the plane, and conversely.

   For convenience the two coordinates are written in parentheses separated by a comma, viz. (*abscissa, ordinate*) always with the abscissa first. Thus $(-5, 2)$ are the coordinates of a point which lies 5 units to the left of the y-axis and 2 units above the x-axis; $(4, 0)$ are the coordinates of a point which lies 4 units to the right of the y-axis on the x-axis; $(0, 0)$ are the coordinates of the origin; (x, y) are the coordinates of a point whose position is unknown or whose position varies.

   e) The algebraic signs of the coordinates of points in the several quadrants are as follows:

   First quadrant, $(+, +)$;   Second quadrant, $(-, +)$;
   Third quadrant, $(-, -)$;   Fourth quadrant, $(+, -)$.

To plot a point is to find the point with the given coordinates. In the next figure the following points have been plotted:

  a) In the first quadrant, $A(1, 3)$, $B(5, 2)$, $C(4, 4)$;
  b) In the second quadrant, $D(-4, 2)$, $E(-6, 4)$, $F(-1, 1)$;
  c) In the third quadrant, $G(-3, -3)$, $H(-1, -5)$, $I(-4, -6)$;
  d) In the fourth quadrant, $J(5, -2)$, $K(2, -5)$, $L(1, -4)$;
  e) On the axes, $M(2, 0)$, $N(-5, 0)$, $Q(0, -4)$, $R(0, 3)$.

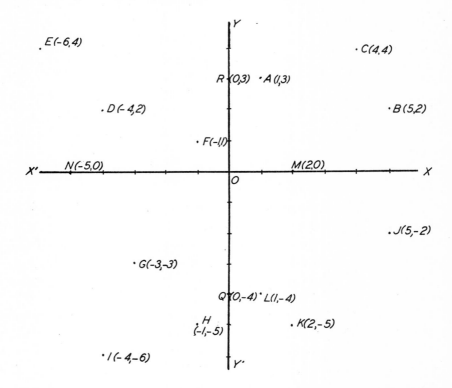

Many cities are laid out with their most important streets forming a rectangular coordinate system. In Chicago (see the accompanying map), the corner of State and Madison is taken as the origin; and directions are given by north, south, east, and west instead of by plus (+) and (−). If we choose to use plus for north and east, minus for south and west, and take one city block as the unit of measure, any corner can be located by use of two signed integers, while houses not on the corners would need two signed fractions. If we take the length of the city block as **100** units, as is customary, it need not be necessary to use fractions.

Using the first scheme, the coordinates of the State-Lake corner are (0, 3) and of the Adams-Michigan corner are (2, −2). What are the coordinates of the corners described as follows:

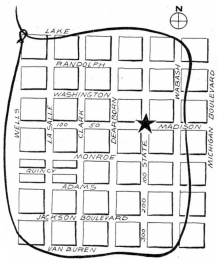

    a) Clark-Van Buren?
    b) Wells-Randolph?
    c) Washington-Dearborn?
    d) State-Jackson?

3. Graphs. Corresponding to the infinite number of solutions (x, y) of an indeterminate equation is an infinite number of points (x, y); i.e., every solution (x, y) of the equation is taken as the coordinates of a point (x, y). The totality of these points constitutes the **graph of the equation** and the equation

Map of Loop

is called the **equation of the graph.** In general, if the equation is a real equation, its graph is a real curve. More precisely, *a curve is the* **graph** *of a given equation and the equation is the equation of the curve if the following two conditions are satisfied:*

    (1) *Every solution* (x, y) *of the equation corresponds to a point on the curve with these numbers as coordinates.*

    (2) *The coordinates* (x, y) *of any point on the curve constitute a solution of the equation.*

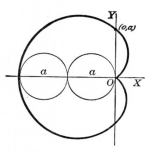

$$x^2 + y^2 + ax = a\sqrt{x^2 + y^2}.$$

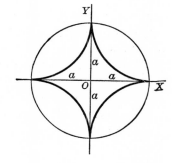

$$x^{\frac{2}{3}} + y^{\frac{2}{3}} = a^{\frac{2}{3}}.$$

In the last figure are shown graphs of functions of y defined by equations. You will not be able to understand how the graphs were constructed, but you should check each one for at least the points whose coordinates are shown. For example, the pair of numbers $(x, y) = \left(\dfrac{-36a}{25}, \dfrac{27a}{25}\right)$ is a solution of the equation $x^2 + y^2 + ax = a\sqrt{x^2 + y^2}$; hence the point with these coordinates is a point on the first curve in the figure.

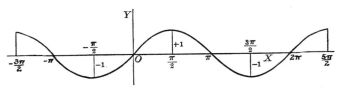

$$y = \sin x.$$

The graph of $y = \sin x$ (where x is the value of the angle) shows that the function y rises and falls and rises and falls (it really goes on forever), becoming zero every time the angle is a multiple of 180°. For any given x, there is only one value of y; while in the graph of $x^3 + y^3 - 3xy = 0$, for some values of x there are three (real) values of y and for other values of x only one real value of y.

It is now possible for you to construct the graphs of simple equations. Since a *graph is a **geometrical picture** of the relationship of the variables as expressed by the equation*, it provides a new and totally different approach to the study of this relationship from that which can be obtained from the equation alone. The truth of this statement becomes more and more apparent with increasing experience in constructing and examining graphs.

A number of examples will be given and their solutions shown. In some of them a geometrical picture is given or a geometrical condition is stated and the corresponding equation is to be found; in others the equation is given and the graph is to be constructed.

EXAMPLE 1. Find the equation of the line which bisects the angle XOY in the figure on the opposite page.

SOLUTION. Any point on the bisector has its ordinate equal to its abscissa, and any point whose ordinate is equal to its abscissa lies on the bisector. Hence the equation of the line AOP is

$$y = x .$$

EXAMPLE 2. Find the graph of the equation $y = -x$.

SOLUTION. The given equation states that the ordinate of each point of the graph is numerically equal to the abscissa but with opposite algebraic sign. This is true of the points on the broken line which bisects the angle YOX' in the figure, since, for the part of the line which lies in the second quadrant, the ordinate is positive and the abscissa negative, while, for the part of the line which lies in the fourth quadrant, the ordinate is negative and the abscissa positive; but for both quadrants the numerical values of the ordinate and abscissa are equal. Hence the graph of the equation $y = -x$ is a line through the origin which is perpendicular to the line AOP in the figure.

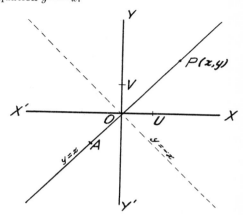

EXAMPLE 3. Find the graph of the equation $x = 0$.

SOLUTION. The given equation may be read "abscissa equals zero." Since abscissa is distance from the y-axis, all points with abscissa equal to zero must lie on the y-axis. Hence *the graph of* $x = 0$ *is the* y-*axis*.

Similarly, *the equation of the* x-*axis is* y $= 0$.

EXAMPLE 4. Find the equation of the line which is parallel to the y-axis and lies three units to its right.

SOLUTION. Since the abscissa of every point on this line is $+3$ and since every point whose abscissa is $+3$ lies on this line, its equation is

$$x = 3 .$$

More generally, the equation **x = *constant*** is the equation of a *vertical line*. When the constant is a positive number, the line lies on the right of the y-axis; when the constant is a negative number, the line lies on the left of the y-axis.

Similarly, **y = *constant*** is the equation of a *horizontal line* which lies above or below the x-axis according as the constant is positive or negative. The accompanying graphs exhibit a number of lines each labeled with its equation.

---

* The equation $x =$ constant or $x = k$ is a linear equation in which the coefficient of y happens to be zero. It stands for $x + 0 \cdot y = k$.

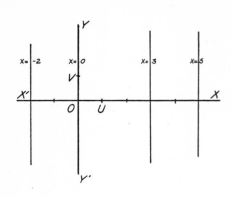

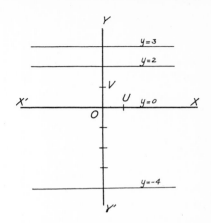

When the properties of a derivative have been discussed (in the next chapter), it will be shown that *the equation of any straight line is a linear equation in two variables*, e.g.,

$$ax+by+c=0 \, ,$$

and that, conversely, *the graph of an arbitrary linear equation in two variables*† (referred to a Cartesian frame of reference) *is a straight line.* Let us accept this statement for the present and plot some straight-line graphs by computing two points on each line, plotting two different lines on a single reference frame.

Equations
a) $x+y-4=0$
b) $x-2y+1=0$
c) $2x+3y+6=0$
d) $3x-y+4=0$

Points
$(1, 3)$ and $(5, -1)$
$(3, 2)$ and $(-1, 0)$
$(0, -2)$ and $(-3, 0)$
$(0, 4)$ and $(-2, -2)$

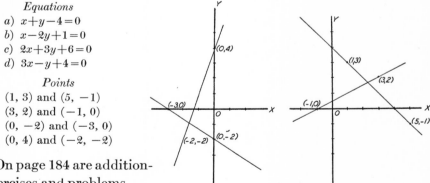

On page 184 are additional exercises and problems.

† The general linear equation $ax+by+c=0$ is an equation in two variables, x and y. However a may be zero, in which case the graph has been shown to be a vertical line; or b may be zero, in which case the graph is a horizontal line. The symbols a and b may not both have the value zero in the same special equation. The value of c may be zero, in which case one solution of the equation is $x=0, y=0$; consequently, one point on the graph is the origin of coordinates.

4. **The temperature scales.** The scales on Fahrenheit and Centigrade thermometers, well known to all, are examples of linear scales. In graduating both of these scales, the two arbitrary points chosen are the positions reached by the column of mercury when it is plunged into melting ice and when it is held in steam at a time when the barometric height is 760 mm. In the Fahrenheit system these two points are labeled 32° and 212°, respectively, while in the Centigrade system they are labeled 0° and 100°. The unit of measure, called 1° F., in the former system is 1/180 of the distance from the freezing-mark to the boiling-mark, while in the latter system the unit, 1° C., is 1/100 of this distance.

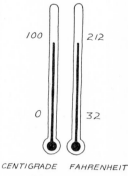

CENTIGRADE   FAHRENHEIT
Thermometers

The two units have the relation 1° C. = 9°/5 F. or 1° F. = 5°/9 C. From these data a known Centigrade reading can be reduced to its equivalent Fahrenheit reading, and conversely. The relationship between these two scales is a linear relationship and, as a consequence of what is promised for the next chapter, can be exhibited geometrically by a straight-line graph (cf. p. 121).

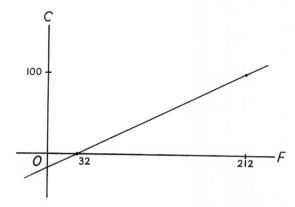

Other examples of linear scales and linear relationships appear in almost every edition of the daily newspapers. They are sometimes given as graphs referred to a Cartesian coordinate system and are sometimes given in the so-called "bar" graphs. We shall return to this subject again.

5. Distance between two points. To find the distance between two points, A and B, whose coordinates are known, we plot the points referred

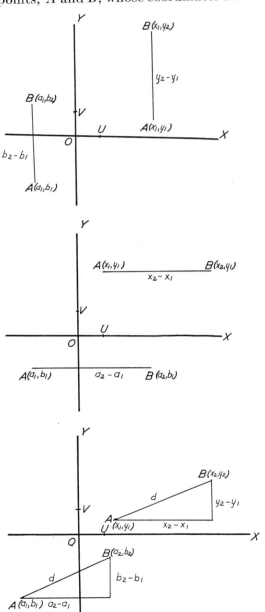

to a rectangular coordinate (Cartesian) frame and draw the line segment AB. There are three cases:

(1) **AB** *is a vertical line segment;* the abscissa of A is the same number as the abscissa of B, but their ordinates are different. Give to the coordinates the following notations:

$$A(x_1, y_1), \qquad B(x_1, y_2).$$

In this case the distance from A to B is given by the signed number $y_2 - y_1$ (cf. p. 83), while the distance from B to A is given by $y_1 - y_2$.

(2) **AB** *is a horizontal line segment;* the ordinate of A is equal to the ordinate of B, but their abscissas are different. Give the coordinates the following notations:

$$A(x_1, y_1), \qquad B(x_2, y_1).$$

In this case the distance from A to B is given by the signed number $x_2 - x_1$, while the distance from B to A is $x_1 - x_2$.

(3) **AB** *is an oblique line segment.* By drawing a horizontal and a perpendicular line segment as indicated in the drawing, we have a right triangle which has AB for its hy-

potenuse. By the theorem of Pythagoras, the square on the hypotenuse is equal to the sum of the squares of the two legs, and we know how to compute the lengths of the two legs from cases (1) and (2). This gives

$$d^2 = (x_2 - x_1)^2 + (y_2 - y_1)^2 ,$$

if we use, as in the figure, d to denote the length of AB and (x_1, y_1), (x_2, y_2), respectively, as the co-ordinates of the given points A and B. We now write

$$d = \sqrt{(x_2 - x_1)^2 + (y_2 - y_1)^2} ,$$

where we take d as positive unless a positive direction has been assigned to the oblique line segment, in which case we choose plus or minus to con-form with the agreement.

EXAMPLES. The distances AB, where A and B have the coordinates indicated be-low, have been computed and are here given. The reader should plot the points and check the results. Additional exercises are on page 184.

A	$(1, 1)$,	$(1, 0)$,	$(-2, 1)$,	$(-4, 0)$,	$(7, -2)$,
B	$(4, 5)$,	$(6, 0)$,	$(1, -3)$,	$(-1, -2)$,	$(-3, 0)$,
$d = AB$	5,	5,	5,	$\sqrt{13}$,	$\sqrt{104}$.

6. Vectors. When vectors are given in a plane in which there is a rectangular coordinate system, convenient analytical expressions can be found for the sum of two or more vectors. To add vector a to vector b, draw equal vectors $\vec{OA} = a$ and $\vec{OB} = b$ from the origin of coordinates and let the coordinates of the termi-nal points be $A(a_1, a_2)$, $B(b_1, b_2)$. Then the coordinates of the ter-minal point C of the sum vector $\vec{OC}$ are $(a_1 + b_1, a_2 + b_2)$. A formu-la for the length c of OC in which the angle θ (cf. p. 72) does not appear can now be found. It is $c^2 = (a_1 + b_1)^2 + (a_2 + b_2)^2$.

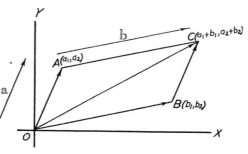

This method shows again that when three or more vectors form a closed polygon their vector sum or resultant is zero (cf. p. 76). For, the

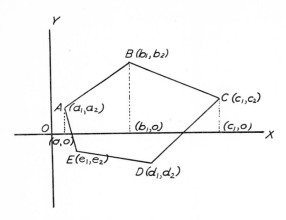

accompanying figure shows that $\bar{a}_1+\bar{b}_1+\bar{c}_1+\bar{d}_1+\bar{e}_1=0$ and also $\bar{a}_2+\bar{b}_2+\bar{c}_2+\bar{d}_2+\bar{e}_2=0$, where $\bar{d}_1$, for example, is the abscissa of the terminal point of a vector from O which is equal to the vector CD.

7. Equation of a circle. The simplest and most obvious application of the distance formula is in writing the equation of a circle. The formula $d^2=(x_2-x_1)^2+(y_2-y_1)^2$ gives the square of the distance from P_1 to P_2. Now suppose that we give to d a fixed value, say r, and take a fixed point for $P_1(x_1, y_1)$, then seek the equation of all of the points whose distance from P_1 is r. (In the figure C is used instead of P_1). The geometrical locus is a circle whose radius is r and whose center is at P_1. Analytically, we say that if $P(x, y)$ is *any point* on this circle, $r^2=(x-x_1)^2+(y-y_1)^2$ and, conversely, if $P(x, y)$ has the property that when its coordinates (x, y) are put into the last

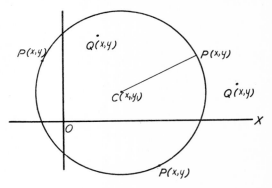

equation the right member becomes the same number as the left member, then P is surely a point on the circle. Thus the equation

$$(x-x_1)^2+(y-y_1)^2=r^2$$

is *the equation of the circle whose center is the point* $P_1(x_1, y_1)$ *and whose radius is* r.

This is really a remarkable formula. By using the symbols x_1 and y_1, instead of actual numbers, for the coordinates of the center of the circle, the result is a formula which may be used for *any center*. Also, by using the number symbol r for the radius, the formula applies for *any radius*.

Furthermore, the variables x and y may stand for *any point* on each of the infinitely many circles. Such a general formula would be impossible without the use of analytical geometry and the relations between points and numbers which it employs. Thus the formula is the equation of all of the circles in the plane, and to give numerical values to x_1, y_1, and r is merely to select out of all the circles in the plane the one with a specified center and radius.

EXAMPLES. The equation $(x-1)^2+(y-3)^2=9$ is the equation of the circle whose center is the point $(1, 3)$ and radius is 3; $(x-1)^2+(y-3)^2=25$ is the equation of the circle whose center is the point $(1, 3)$ and radius is 5; $(x+2)^2+(y-4)^2=1$ is the equation of the unit circle (a circle whose radius is unity is called a "unit circle") whose center is the point $(-2, 4)$; and $x^2+y^2=4$ is the equation of the circle whose center is the origin of coordinates and radius is 2.

The reader should appreciate the fact that he does not have to do any computing in order to know the coordinates of the center and the length of the radius; all that he needs do is *look*, for they are in plain sight.

Let it be required to write the equation of the circle whose center is the point $(5, 0)$ and radius is 10; the equation is $(x-5)^2+y^2=100$. Again, all of the circles in the plane whose center is the origin of coordinates are given by the single equation

$$x^2+y^2=r^2 .$$

A special one of these circles is obtained by giving to r a numerical value.

It will be a good exercise for you to write down the radii and the coordinates of the centers of the circles whose equations follow and to check your work with the answers in the back of the book (p. 186). Also, you should answer the questions regarding them which follow.

a) $x^2+(y-3)^2=4$, e) $(x-2)^2+(y+3)^2=4$,
b) $(x-2)^2+y^2=4$, f) $(x+2)^2+(y+3)^2=4$,
c) $(x-2)^2+(y-3)^2=4$, g) $x^2+y^2=2$.
d) $(x+2)^2+(y-3)^2=4$,

1. Which, if any, of the circles whose equations are given above have a radius of 2? Of 3? Of 4?

2. Which have a center lying in quadrant *I*? *II*? *III*? *IV*? On the x-axis? On the y-axis?

3. What is the distance between the centers of circles c and d? c and e? c and f?

4. What is the equation of the circle obtained by moving circle (b) 3 units to the right? 3 units up? 3 units down?

5. A cow is tied with a 30-ft. rope to a tree which stands 10 ft. north of an east-west fence and 20 ft. east of a north-south fence. What is the equation of the circle which limits the grazing area of the cow? Can the cow graze over the whole circle? What is the distance of the tree from the fence corner? What is the equation of the east-west line through the tree? Of the north-south line through it?

8. Variables and functions.

Attention has been repeatedly called to the fact that

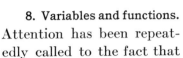

Cow ponders length of rope

an equation in two symbols is an expression of a *relationship* between the quantities represented by the symbols. For example, if in the linear equation $4x+y-2=0$ an arbitrary value is given to x, the corresponding value of y is found by substituting for x in the expression $-4x+2$. The value of the expression, $-4x+2$, depends on the value assigned to x; it is called a **function** of x, and is, in fact, a *linear* function of x. But from the given equation we may write

$$y = -4x+2 .$$

Hence, the symbol y is a symbol which is here being used to designate the function $-4x+2$.

We say "the equation defines y as a function of x," since for every value assigned to x a corresponding value of y can be computed from the relationship between x and y which is given by the equation. We may just as well say "the equation defines x as a function of y," since, when arbitrary values are assigned to y, the corresponding values of x can be computed by $x = -\frac{1}{4}y+\frac{1}{2}$.

Both x and y are called **variables**, since their values are not assumed to remain unchanged. When we write

$$y = -4x+2 ,$$

we are thinking of x as the **independent variable**, i.e., the one to which the arbitrary values are to be assigned; consequently, y is a **dependent variable**, since its value depends on the value assigned to x. Thus the phrase "dependent variable" means exactly the same as the word "function," which was defined above.

When the last equation is written $x = -\frac{1}{4}y + \frac{1}{2}$, y is to be looked upon as the independent variable and x as the dependent variable.

Quite a different type of relationship between the two variables is expressed by the equation $3x^2 - y + 7 = 0$. It defines y as a *quadratic function of x; viz.,*

$$y = 3x^2 + 7 ,$$

and it defines x as a *double-valued* function of y; viz.,

$$x = \pm \sqrt{\frac{y-7}{3}} .$$

In linear equations there has been no limitation as to the arbitrary values which could be assigned to the independent variable, but it is apparent from the last equation that imaginary values of x will be obtained if a value less than 7 should be assigned to y. For, set $y = 6$, then $x = \sqrt{-1/3}$; set $y = 1$, and get $x = \sqrt{-2}$; set $y = -2$ and get $x = \sqrt{-3}$; etc. Values of y which are greater than or equal to 7 are called **admissible values** for this equation, since for them x^2 is a positive number (or zero) and hence x itself is real,

Consider, now, the equation $x^2 + y^2 = 25$ whose graph is known to be a circle with radius equal to 5 and center at the origin of coordinates. If x is the independent variable, the double-valued function y is given by

$$y = \pm \sqrt{25 - x^2} .$$

Admissible values of x are those for which $|x| \leq 5$.* When x is assigned an admissible value, say $x = 4$, there are two real values of y which correspond to it. They are, in this case, $y = 3$ and $y = -3$. Hence, on the circle there are two points with abscissa 4.

Let y be the independent variable in the same equation. Then the equation defines x as a double-valued function of y as follows:

$$x = \pm \sqrt{25 - y^2} .$$

Admissible values of y are those for which $|y| = 5$.
A more complicated equation is the following:

$$x^5 - 7x^2y^3 + 3x - 5y^2 - 10 = 0 .$$

---

* The symbol $|x|$ is used to denote the numerical value of x. Thus $|-5| = |5| = 5$.

For every x there are three values of y, and for every y there are five values of x; i.e., the equation defines y as a three-valued function of x and it defines x as a five-valued function of y. It is possible to solve for y as a function of x, but the expression thus obtained would contain both a square root sign and a cube root sign; hence in general we prefer to make the substitution of numerical values of x in the equation as it stands, after which we should seek the three corresponding values of y (the three roots of the cubic equation). It is not possible (Abel's theorem) to write out a formula for x, viz.,

$x =$ *an expression containing* y *and the operational symbols of arithmetic,*

but assigned values of y may be substituted in the equation as it stands and the corresponding values of x obtained by finding the roots of the quintic equation thus arising.

To proceed with the discussion of functions and their graphs which was abandoned for a digression on admissible values of the independent variable, we remark that, when there is no reason for the contrary choice, it is customary to let x represent the independent variable and y the function. With this agreement, when the graph of an equation is con-structed *the ordinates of the points on the curve are the values of the function.* In the accompanying figure, let the coordinates of A, B, etc., be (a_1, a_2), (b_1, b_2), etc. Let us imagine that this curve is the path of a point which started at the left beyond the confines of the paper and traced the curve, moving in the direction of increasing abscissas. Since ordinate $=$ function, from inspection of the graph the following remarks can be made about the function and the curve which is its geometrical representation:

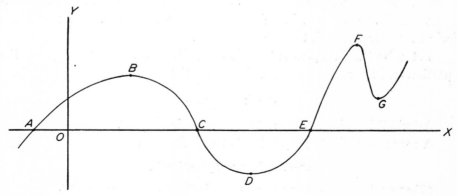

The function	*The curve*
The function is zero for $x = a_1, c_1, e_1$.	The curve crosses the x-axis at A, C, E.
The function is positive for $a_1 < x < c_1$ and for $x > e_1$.	The curve lies above the x-axis between the points A and C and after the point E.
The function is increasing as x changes (increases) from a_1 to b_1, from d_1 to f_1, and from g_1 on.	The curve is rising from A to B, from D to F, and from G on.
The values b_1 and f_1 are called **maximum values of the function**; the values d_1 and g_1 are called **minimum values of the function**.	The points B, F, D, and G are called turning points on the curve, B and F being **maximum points** and D and G **minimum points**.

The words "maximum" and "minimum" are used here in a technical sense. Maximum value of the function, for example, does not mean (as one might well suppose) the greatest value which the function attains for any value of x but, merely, the greatest value which it attains when, having been increasing, it ceases increasing and begins to decrease. In other words, *the ordinate of a maximum point on a curve* is greater than the ordinates of other nearby points.* In a similar manner *the ordinate of a minimum point is less than the ordinates of other nearby points.*

Inspection of the last graph also shows that sometimes the curve is rising or falling much more rapidly than at other times; i.e., the rate at which the function changes varies with the value of the independent variable. Analytic geometry can give us no aid in the study of this topic; that is the province of the calculus, and it will be treated in the next chapter.

9. **Applications.** We shall obtain the formula for the **coordinates of the mid-point** of a line segment when the coordinates of its end-points are known. This formula, with what has already been explained about analytic geometry, will enable us to prove analytically a number of theorems of elementary geometry. In most cases the analytical proof is simpler than the synthetic proof.

Let the end-points of a given line segment be denoted by $P_1(x_1, y_1)$ and $P_2(x_2, y_2)$ and let $P(x, y)$ be the mid-point of the line segment. Draw

---

* The definitions of "maximum" and "minimum" require the tacit assumption that the graph does not break at the point under discussion, i.e., that the function is changing continuously.

354-59

P_1M_1, PM, P_2M_2 perpendicular to the x-axis, as in the figure. The length of M_1M_2 is x_2-x_1; then $M_1M=\frac{1}{2}(x_2-x_1)$ and $OM=OM_1+M_1M=x_1+\frac{1}{2}(x_2-x_1)=\frac{1}{2}(x_1+x_2)$. This shows that the abscissa of the mid-point is the average of the two abscissas. By drawing perpendiculars from P_1, P, and P_2 to the y-axis and making a similar computation, it is found that *the ordinate of the mid-point is equal to the average of the two ordinates.* Hence the coordinates of the mid-point $P(x, y)$ are given by

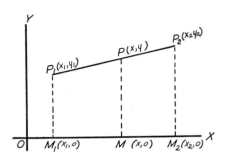

$$x=\tfrac{1}{2}(x_1+x_2) , \qquad y=\tfrac{1}{2}(y_1+y_2) .$$

EXAMPLE. The mid-point of the line segment which joins $(4, 3)$ to $(2, -7)$ is $(3, -2)$. A sketch will show that this is correct.

Theorem I. The mid-point of the hypotenuse of a right triangle is equidistant from the three vertices.

PROOF. Take the origin of coordinates at the vertex of the right angle and let the legs of the triangle extend along the two axes, as in the figure. Let the coordinates of the vertex A be $(a, 0)$ and of B, $(0, b)$, and let K be the mid-point of the hypotenuse. Then the coordinates of K are $(\frac{1}{2}a, \frac{1}{2}b)$.

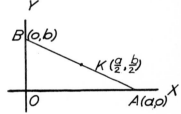

The proof is completed by showing that the length of AK is equal to the length of OK. These two lengths, computed by the distance formula, are

$$AK=\sqrt{(\tfrac{1}{2}a-a)^2+(\tfrac{1}{2}b-0)^2}=\sqrt{\tfrac{1}{4}a^2+\tfrac{1}{4}b^2} ,$$

$$OK=\sqrt{(\tfrac{1}{2}a-0)^2+(\tfrac{1}{2}b-0)^2}=\sqrt{\tfrac{1}{4}a^2+\tfrac{1}{4}b^2} .$$

Theorem 2. The line joining the mid-points of two sides of a triangle is equal to half the third side.

PROOF. We may take the origin of coordinates at one vertex of the triangle and let the x-axis extend along the base of the triangle, as in the figure; but we cannot give numerical values to the coordinates of B

and the abscissa of A if we wish to be perfectly general. With the notations chosen, the coordinates of the mid-points of the two sides are $B_1(\frac{1}{2}b, \frac{1}{2}c)$ and $A_1[\frac{1}{2}(a+b), \frac{1}{2}c]$, and the length of B_1A_1 is $\sqrt{[\frac{1}{2}(a+b)-\frac{1}{2}b]^2+(\frac{1}{2}c-\frac{1}{2}c)^2}=\sqrt{\frac{1}{4}a^2}=\frac{1}{2}a$. But this is exactly half the length of OA; hence the theorem is proved.

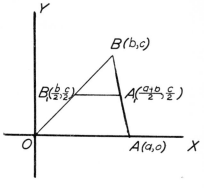

Theorem 3. The diagonals of a rectangle are equal.

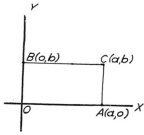

PROOF. Let two sides of the rectangle extend along the coordinate axes, as in the figure; and let the length and width of the rectangle be denoted by a and b, respectively. Then the coordinates of A, B, and C are, respectively,

$$(a, 0), \qquad (0, b), \qquad (a, b).$$

The length of OC is $\sqrt{a^2+b^2}$, and the length of AB is $\sqrt{(a-0)^2+(0-b)^2}=\sqrt{a^2+b^2}$.

These examples are given here to emphasize the statement, made several times previously, that the linking of algebra and geometry by the happy idea of Descartes gave us a tool well suited for pushing outward the frontiers of mathematical knowledge. The reader should not think, however, that the Cartesian system of coordinates is the only system which is powerful. It is the simplest system and is therefore used more in elementary texts than any other. In the next section an entirely different frame of reference for a coordinate system will be explained and some of its uses shown. But these are merely the beginning. In such coordinate systems as these, the point is the fundamental element. It is located by a set of numbers (two if the points considered lie in the same plane, three if they lie in ordinary space, four if they lie in a space of four dimensions, etc.) which constitute a solution of an indeterminate equation. Another way of applying these principles is to associate points with a given system of curves. Corresponding to two distinct points, A and B, are two distinct curves, graphs of two equations

$$f(x, y) = 0 \quad \text{and} \quad F(x, y) = 0 \,;$$

and for every point on the line determined by A and B, there is a corresponding curve of the pencil of curves determined by the graphs of $f(x, y) = 0$ and $F(x, y) = 0$.*

There is no limit to the extent of application of this method of association. By its use, the various fields of geometry have been enriched beyond measure.

10. Polar coordinates. Locating points in a plane by means of a system of Cartesian coordinates has been compared to giving directions in a city—a certain number of blocks east, for example, then a certain number of blocks south. When the system of polar coordinates is used, it may be compared to giving directions on a prairie or a desert where a place is located by its distance and direction from a given point.

Let O be a given point called the **pole** and OX drawn to the right from O be the line, called the **prime direction,** from which directions are to be

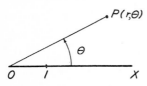

measured. Choose a unit of length and indicate it on OX. Take P any point in the plane (cf. the accompanying figure) and let r denote the length of OP measured in the chosen linear unit and θ the angle (any one of the angles) through which OX may turn in order to take the direction of OP. We agree that when OX turns *counterclockwise* to reach OP the angle will be a **positive angle;** otherwise it is negative. There is, then, no limitation on the size of an angle. The minute hand of a clock, for example, generates an angle of $-360°$ in 1 hr. and an angle of $-1{,}980°$ in $5\frac{1}{2}$ hr. The two coordinates r and θ, (r, θ), serve to locate P without ambiguity.

To plot points and construct graphs in polar coordinates it is convenient to use polar coordinate paper. This paper has rays radiating at regular intervals from the pole with a linear scale on the rays for measuring r and a circular scale for measuring the angles.

---

* Symbols like $f(x, y)$, read "f of x, y"; or "function of x and y" are used to indicate an expression depending on x and y when it is not necessary to be explicit as to the nature of the function.

The line OP is called the **radius vector** of the point P; θ is the **vectorial** angle. For a pair of values (r, θ) given as the coordinates of a point, there is one and only one point with these coordinates. When a point is given, however, its coordinates are not unique. For example, if the angle θ in the last figure is 30° and the length of OP is 3, the point P is denoted by $(3, 30°)$, $(3, -330°)$, $(-3, -150°)$, $(-3, 210°)$, and by other pairs of numbers obtained by replacing the foregoing angles by other angles which differ from them by integral multiples of 360°.

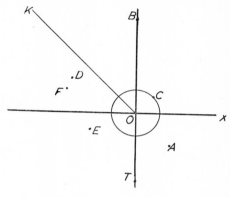

In the figure the points labeled A, B, etc., have been plotted from the following table of coordinates:

$$A(2, -30°), \quad B(4, 90°), \quad C(1, 45°),$$
$$D(3, 150°), \quad E(2, 200°), \quad F(3, -200°).$$

The circle is the graph of the equation $r = 1$; and the half-rays OT and OK, respectively, are the graphs of the equations $\theta = 270°$ and $\theta = -225°$.

CHAPTER 6

THE DIFFERENTIAL CALCULUS

THE calculus is modern. Compared in age with arithmetic, algebra, geometry, and trigonometry, it is a mere babe in arms; but compared with them as to power and extent of achievement, it is a giant—indeed a supergiant. The story of the independent invention of the calculus by Newton, the natural scientist, and Leibniz, the philosopher, has been related in chapter 3. These men did not "reach out into thin air and gather in" this remarkable new mathematical idea; indeed, others before them had, for a long time, been working on the problems which led to the discovery of the processes of the differential and integral calculus.

We have already mentioned the fact that Euclid did not *create* what is now known as Euclidean geometry but that he made a threefold contribution to geometry which *changed a mass of data into a* **science**. This contribution consisted in (*a*) *putting it on a logical foundation of definitions and assumptions,* (*b*) **organizing** *geometrical facts most of which had long been known to his predecessors,* and (*c*) *formulating precise proofs of relationships which had previously been accepted as intuitive or for which incorrect proofs had been given.* In much the same manner, all important scientific concepts and methods evolve; in fact, scientific truths can evolve in no other way. The predecessors of Newton and Leibniz had been working on such problems as drawing tangents to curves, finding the lengths of curves,* finding the areas inclosed by curves, and finding the volumes inclosed by surfaces. These problems, when solvable, are readily handled by the methods of the calculus, but when the attention is centered on problems of this type, it is possible to miss entirely the *fundamental notion underlying the differential calculus, the notion of* **rate of change.** This is exactly what the predecessors of Newton and Leibniz (with the exception of Fermat) did; and the power of the two discoverers came from the fact that they had the vision of a *dynamic* concept—that of rate of change. We repeat, however, that they could not have succeeded in developing their ideas and in making the far-reaching applications if the way had not been prepared for them by those who had gone before.

An incontestable claim of mathematics to importance in our civilization is that it is indispensable in a scientific explanation of what we observe in nature, i.e., the phenomena of nature. Of the several fields of elementary mathematics, the calculus may be called the *motion-picture machine* of mathematics which catches natural phenomena *in the act of changing,* or, as Newton called it, *in a state of flux.* Other fields of mathematics are to be likened to the camera which shows a *still* picture (of nature) as it appears at a given instant without regard to the possible appearance the following instant.

It takes only a small amount of observation and reflection to convince us that nature is never static, that everything about us is either in a state of flux or a state of motion; hence a true understanding and interpretation of the processes of nature is not possible apart from the notion of rate of change.

1. Rate of change. Before discussing instantaneous rate of change, it is desirable to have definitely in mind the well-known concepts of **uniform velocity** and **average velocity** of a moving object, as well as the less familiar concepts of **uniform rate of change** and **average rate of change** of a function which is changing. When the velocity is uniform, the moving object passes over *equal distances in equal intervals of time;* when a function of a variable x is changing uniformly, it changes *equal amounts for equal changes in x.* The last statements are equivalent to these: When the motion is uniform, distances traversed are proportional to periods of time;

---

* The reader will recall that in Euclidean geometry lengths are computed for straight lines and circles only; plane areas for figures bounded by lines and arcs of circles; and volumes for solids bounded by planes and spherical surfaces.

and when the change in the function is uniform, changes in the function are proportional to changes in the independent variable.

In this as well as in the following sections, a statement about a moving object is followed by a similar statement about a changing function. The two notions are basically the same; in both cases there is change, in the one a change in distance, in the other a change in value.

When the velocity is not uniform, the *average velocity over a given period of time* is obtained by dividing the distance traversed during this time by the time itself, i.e., average velocity per second for a given t seconds is equal to s/t where s is the distance traversed during the t seconds under consideration. Similarly, *average rate of change of a function y (y = function of x) per unit of change in x* is equal to $\Delta y/\Delta x$ where Δx denotes the amount of change in x under consideration and Δy is the corresponding change in y.

Note. The symbol Δx is read "delta x" and also "increment of x." It usually means "a little more of x," since it is generally used to denote that a small amount has been added to x, while Δy (increment of y) gives the amount of change in y. For example, if x is changed from 3 to 3.1, $\Delta x = 0.1$; if the change of x from 3 to 3.1 causes y to change from 7 to 6.5, then $\Delta x = 0.1$ and $\Delta y = -0.5$. Thus the average change in y per unit of change in x when $\Delta x = 0.1$ and $x = 3$ is $-0.5 \div 0.1 = -5$. We say that *during the interval under consideration y is decreasing on the average five times as fast as x is increasing.*

As stated in the first sentence of this section, the preceding concepts are not new. The new concepts which the differential calculus brings to us are: (*a*) **velocity at a given instant or instantaneous* velocity** and (*b*) **instantaneous rate of change.**

If a moving object were equipped with a speedometer, if there were no lag in the action of the speedometer, and if an accurate reading could be automatically recorded for every second, there would be no obscurity connected with the meaning of "instantaneous velocity"; a reading of 20 would mean a velocity of 20 linear units per unit of time, e.g., feet per second or miles per hour. In the latter case, we should not for a moment conclude that the moving object would go 20 mi. during the next hour, or 10 mi. during the next half-hour; the reading would be interpreted to mean that *if the motion is* **uniform** *and remains so for an hour* or *if it were*

---

* The concept "instantaneous velocity" is not new; what the differential calculus brings is a method of ascertaining instantaneous velocity when the law which governs the motion of the moving body can be expressed in mathematical symbols.

suddenly to become and remain **uniform** *at a reading of 20,* the distance traversed during the next hour would be 20 mi.

In the case of a falling body with no speedometer attached to supply us with readings, how can a meaning to the phrase *instantaneous velocity* be arrived at? A method which suggests itself to a scientific mind is to perform an experiment or a number of experiments and see whether results can be obtained which may be used as a basis for a definition. We shall attempt to devise an experiment as free as possible from the errors of measuring and observing.

Let a motion-picture camera which makes sixteen exposures to the second be used to photograph a ball shot vertically into the air with an initial velocity of 100 ft. per sec. Let the film thus obtained be thrown on a screen on which there is a vertical linear scale so that the position of the ball with respect to the ground (i.e., the distance from the ground) can be accurately marked on the screen for each one-sixteenth of a second. In order to arrive at an estimate of the speed of the ball at the end of the first second ($t=1$), the following facts were noted:

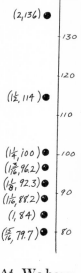

a) Starting with $t=1$, when t changes from $t=1$ to $t=2$, s changes from $s=84$ to $s=136$, an increase of 52 ft.

b) Starting with $t=1$, when t changes from $t=1$ to $t=1\frac{1}{2}$, s changes from $s=84$ to $s=114$, an increase of 30 ft.

These data and the data used below are taken from the figure at the right, where the positions of the ball with respect to the vertical scale are shown from $t=\frac{15}{16}$ sec. to $t=2$ sec. The facts of (*a*) and (*b*) above can be given in much more compact form by using Δt for the time *after* $t=1$ and Δs for the distance *above 84 ft.* The average speed for the time Δt under consideration is then given by the quotient $\Delta s/\Delta t$. Let us now re-write (*a*) and (*b*) in the more compact form and follow by similar entries for smaller values of Δt. We have

a) $\Delta t=1$, $\Delta s=52$, $\Delta s/\Delta t=52$ ft./sec.
b) $\Delta t=\frac{1}{2}$, $\Delta s=30$, $\Delta s/\Delta t=30\div\frac{1}{2}=60$ ft./sec.
c) $\Delta t=\frac{1}{4}$, $\Delta s=16$, $\Delta s/\Delta t=16\div\frac{1}{4}=64$ ft./sec.
d) $\Delta t=\frac{3}{16}$, $\Delta s=12.2$, $\Delta s/\Delta t=12.2\div\frac{3}{16}=65.1$ ft./sec.
e) $\Delta t=\frac{1}{8}$, $\Delta s=8.3$, $\Delta s/\Delta t=8.3\div\frac{1}{8}=66.4$ ft./sec.
f) $\Delta t=\frac{1}{16}$, $\Delta s=4.2$, $\Delta s/\Delta t=4.2\div\frac{1}{16}=67.2$ ft./sec.

The last entry in the tabulation above shows that for the first sixteenth of a second after $t=1$, the average speed of the ball was 67.2 ft. per sec. If data could be secured for $t=1\frac{1}{32}$, the average speed for the first thirty-second of a second after $t=1$ would be a number greater than 67.2 but certainly not much greater. If we agree to accept, say, 68 ft. per sec. as the instantaneous speed at the time $t=1$, we can be certain that this number is *an excellent approximation* of the actual speed with which the ball was moving at that instant. The process of **differentiation or finding the derivative** which will be explained in the next section gives the *precise value* of the instantaneous speed of an object which is moving, when the law which governs its motion is known.

Let a similar examination be now made of *a function of x which changes with x*, say the function

$$y = x^2 - 3 .$$

As x increases from $x=0$, y also increases. To get an approximation to the *rate of change of y with respect to x* when x has the value 2, we compute the *average rate of change of y as compared with* the change in x for small changes in x (i.e., for small values of Δx).

x	Δx	y	Δy	$\Delta y/\Delta x$
2......	......	1	....	.....
3......	1	6	5	5
$2\frac{1}{2}$......	$\frac{1}{2}$	$3\frac{1}{4}$	$2\frac{1}{4}$	$4\frac{1}{2}$
$2\frac{1}{4}$......	$\frac{1}{4}$	2	1	$4\frac{1}{4}$
2.1.....	0.1	1.41	0.41	4.1
2.01....	0.01	1.0401	0.0401	4.01
2.001...	0.001	1.004001	0.004001	4.001

The conclusion is that when $x=2$ and is increasing, y is changing (also increasing) approximately four times as fast as x is changing. Because of the way in which this conclusion was obtained, it must be looked upon as an approximation, though undoubtedly an excellent one. All of the entries in the table are exact, since they were obtained by computation and not by observation or measurement.

2. The derivative.   In the last paragraphs we computed approximations to the instantaneous rate of change of y with respect to x when $y=x^2$; in fact, we actually computed six approximations each one better than the preceding. Although we stopped with $\Delta x = 0.001$, an inspection of the last three results convinces us that we can write down better and better approximations without further computation; e.g., for $\Delta x = 0.0001$, $\Delta y/\Delta x = 4.0001$; for $\Delta x = 0.00001$, $\Delta y/\Delta x = 4.00001$, etc. Hence it is clear that *as close an approximation to $\Delta y/\Delta x$ as is desired can be obtained by taking Δx sufficiently small.* Furthermore, in any similar situation if we knew how to continue indefinitely the process of getting better and better approximations, the limit of these would of course be the true value.

The calculus gives us a method of doing this, a method which (happily for us) is far easier to apply to particular problems than would be expected from the ideas of approximations and limits which are involved. The simplification arises from the fact that we do not need to give to Δx a sequence of numerical values and complete the corresponding numerical values of Δy and of $\Delta y/\Delta x$, but we may keep the symbol Δx before us and compute $\Delta y/\Delta x$ *in terms of the symbols x and Δx.* We shall then have a *formula for average rate of change* whose limit when Δx approaches zero can be seen at a glance. The work (applied to the function of the last paragraph, $y = x^2 - 3$) proceeds as follows:

1) For each x the value of y is given by $x^2 - 3$.
2) When $x = x + \Delta x$, the new value of the function is computed by

$$y + \Delta y = (x + \Delta x)^2 - 3^* = x^2 + 2x(\Delta x) + (\Delta x)^2 - 3 .$$

3) Subtract y from the left member and its equal, $x^2 - 3$, from the right member and get

$$\Delta y = 2x(\Delta x) + (\Delta x)^2 .$$

By this formula can be computed *the increment of y which corresponds to any increment Δx of x.* Its value depends on x as well as on the value assigned to Δx. Let both members of the last equation be divided by Δx. The result,

$$\frac{\Delta y}{\Delta x} = 2x + \Delta x ,$$

is an expression for the *average change in y per unit of change in x,* and it is a function of both x and Δx. Let a numerical value be assigned to x, say

---

* The two formulas $(a+b)^2 = a^2 + 2ab + b^2$ and $(a+b)^3 = a^3 + 3a^2b + 3ab^2 + b^3$ come from elementary algebra. They can be obtained by multiplication.

$x=2$, as in section 1. Then the average change in y per unit of change in x when x changes from 2 to $2+\Delta x$ is

$$\frac{\Delta y}{\Delta x}=4+\Delta x \ .$$

To show that we have here, in a formula, the same information that we had in section 1, we need only give to Δx the values which were used there, viz., 1, 0.5, 0.1, 0.01, 0.0001, and compare the numbers obtained with the entries in the last column of the table. From the formula, it is clear that the limit as Δx approaches zero is 4. In symbols we write

$$\lim_{\Delta x \to 0} \frac{\Delta y}{\Delta x}= \lim_{\Delta x \to 0} (4+\Delta x)=4 \ .$$

The next section is devoted to the discussion of limits and their evaluation—a topic of prime importance in view of the following facts:

a) The derivative of a single-valued function of x is, by definition, the limit as Δx approaches zero of $\Delta y/\Delta x$, *if the limit exists.*

b) The derivative of a function gives its rate of change.

c) The fundamental notion of the differential calculus is rate of change. Natural phenomena are characterized by motion or by change.

Before rate of change can be discussed more completely, more must be known of the evaluation of limits.

3. Limit. As an example, a driver has applied the brakes to his car; an assistant watches the speedometer and records the readings as fast as he can write them down. He writes

$$60, \ 50, \ 40, \ 32, \ 24, \ 18, \ 12, \ 8, \ 5, \ 3, \ 2, \ 1.$$

This is a sequence of values of v (velocity), which has zero as a limit,

$$\lim v=0$$

Again, suppose that a driver going 32 mi. per hr. has applied his brakes 100 ft. from a train. If a mechanic who knows the car thoroughly says the car will be going 16 mi. per hr. after 50 ft., 8 mi. per hr. after 75 ft., 4 mi. per hr. after $87\frac{1}{2}$ ft., ... , we conclude that the car will stop *just in time*, i.e., the car will not go more than 100 ft. If we designate the distance passed over by the car after the brakes were applied by s, then the foregoing tabulation shows that there is a definite relationship between s and v, and we can write

$$\lim_{v \to 0} s = 100 ,$$

Train and car problem

read "the limit of s, as v approaches zero, is 100."

More generally, let the distance from the origin of a point P on the x-axis be denoted, as usual, by its abscissa x, and let P take a succession of positions on $X'OX$, each time diminishing its distance from a fixed point A until the numerical value of its distance from A *becomes and remains less than any previously assigned small positive number*. Then x, the abscissa of P, is said to approach a, the abscissa of A, as a limit, and we write

$$\lim x = a .$$

Now let us suppose that y is a function of x and let us see what y is doing while the independent variable x is approaching a value, say a, as a

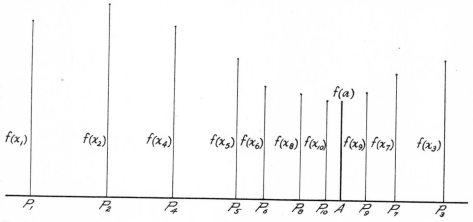

limit. We must assume that the value of y can be computed for all values of x, say x_1, x_2, etc., which correspond to points on a line segment which contains $A(a, 0)$ (as in the figure), except possibly for the number a itself. As x takes a succession of values, $x_1, x_2, \ldots$, approaching a as a limit, y takes a succession of values*

$$y_1 = f(x_1) , \qquad y_2 = f(x_2) , \ldots$$

Of the numerous situations which may arise, by far the most delightful is for the numbers $f(x_1)$, $f(x_2)$, etc., to approach as a limit *the number which is found by substituting a for x in $f(x)$*. We then say that as x approaches the limit a, $f(x)$ approaches the limit $f(a)$, or, with a slightly different wording, *the limit, as x approaches a, of $f(x)$ is $f(a)$*. It is the latter wording which is generally used in reading the symbolic expression for the situation described, viz.,

$$\lim_{x \to a} f(x) = f(a) .$$

Note. In this book it is not possible to study the more complicated situations which may arise in the evaluation of limits. A reader who is interested may read the chapter on limits in any good calculus text. We pause, however, to give examples in which limits cannot be evaluated by mere substitution as above.

EXAMPLE 1. Evaluate $\lim\limits_{x \to 2} \dfrac{5}{x-2}$. By substituting $x=2$, we get $\dfrac{5}{0}$. But division by zero is not permitted in our number system; hence there is no quotient of 5 by 0, and we say $f(2)$ *does not exist*.

EXAMPLE 2. Evaluate $\lim\limits_{x \to 3} \dfrac{2x-6}{x^2-9}$. On substituting $x=3$, we get $\dfrac{0}{0}$. Strange as it may seem to the unitiated, this symbol cannot be disposed of as readily as 5/0 by a wave of the hand and an "$f(3)$ does not exist." Experience has shown that it is sometimes possible to find other ways of evaluating limits *when the substitution method does not work*, and that it sometimes happens that a function which becomes 0/0 by substitution really has a limit, while another function which becomes 0/0 by substitution may have no limit as x approaches the value under consideration. For these reasons, when 0/0 is obtained one cannot say that this function has no limit; nor can one say that this function has a limit. It seems reasonable, then, to say that 0/0 is an **indeterminate form**; and this is the terminology which is in common use.

No other method of evaluation, however, can find a limit for a function which, on substitution, becomes 5/0 or $k/0$ where k is any real number not itself zero.

There is a third case which may arise in the evaluation of limits. We may get a number $f(a)$ by substituting $x=a$ in $f(x)$ but may find that the limit as x approaches a of $f(x)$ is a number b *different from $f(a)$*. Examples of this type require rather complicated algebra for their investigation, and hence no example is given here.

---

* The symbol $f(x)$ is frequently used to denote a function of x whose nature need not be specified; the number obtained by replacing x by a number, say x_1, is then denoted by $f(x_1)$.

The description of these cases should keep the reader from feeling that the subject is trivial when, in all examples which arise in this book—and, in fact, in the majority of cases met in pure and applied mathematics—in computing derivatives the answers fall out by mere substitution.

A little computation will show that the following limits are correct.

$$\lim_{x \to 1} (5x^2+3)=8 , \qquad\qquad \lim_{m \to 0} (6m+4)^2=16 ,$$

$$\lim_{x \to -1} \frac{2}{x-5} = -\frac{1}{3} , \qquad\qquad \lim_{k \to 4} \frac{2x^2+4k}{k-1} = \frac{2x^2+16}{3} ,$$

$$\lim_{t \to 0} (7t^2-5)=-5 , \qquad\qquad \lim_{\Delta x \to 0} \frac{4x+3(\Delta x)}{5+(\Delta x)^2} = \frac{4x}{5} ,$$

$$\lim_{x \to 3} \frac{7}{x-3} \text{ does not exist}, \qquad \lim_{x \to 2} \frac{x^2+4x-1}{x^2-4} \text{ does not exist},$$

$$\lim_{t \to 1} \frac{3t^2-3t}{t^2-1} \text{ is indeterminate}, \qquad \lim_{x \to 0} \frac{3x^2+4x}{2x^2-x} \text{ is indeterminate}.$$

4. Computation of derivatives. The definition of the derivative of y with respect to x as given in section 2, page 110, may now be restated in the notation of limits. As before, for simplicity, we restrict ourselves to single-valued functions and write as a *definition:*

The derivative of y with respect to x, denoted by the symbol $D_x y,$*is given by

$$\lim_{\Delta x \to 0} \frac{\Delta y}{\Delta x} ,$$

if the limit exists. In the formula, Δx is an arbitrary increment of the independent variable and is required to approach zero, while Δy is the corresponding increment of the dependent variable or function.

Lest it be forgotten, we recall that the word *derivative* is merely a word adopted for convenience to replace the more cumbersome phrase *instantaneous rate of change.* In other words, if we can compute the derivative of a function of x (the derivative will also be a function of x) and can find its value for, say $x=a$, the *number* thus found tells how fast y is changing with respect to x at the point on the graph whose abscissa is a.

In the case of a moving object where the distance traversed is a known function of the time, $s=F(t)$, the derivative of s with respect to t

---

* The symbol $D_x y$ is read "the derivative of y with respect to x." When the independent variable is the time t and the dependent variable is the distance s, the symbol $D_t s$ stands for "the derivative of s with respect to t."

gives the rate of change of distance with respect to time, i.e., it gives the *speed*. Hence,

$$D_t s = \text{speed}^* = \lim_{\Delta t \to 0} \frac{\Delta s}{\Delta t} .$$

To compute a derivative, then, we must add an increment to x, compute the corresponding increment of y, divide Δy by Δx to get the average rate of change of y with respect to x, then find the limiting value of the expression thus obtained as Δx approaches zero (*if the limit exists and if we can find it*). Examples are given in the next section.

5. Differentiation of cx^2. Let $y = cx^2(c \neq 0)$. When an increment is added to x we have

$$y + \Delta y = c(x + \Delta x)^2 = c[x^2 + 2x(\Delta x) + (\Delta x)^2] .$$

Subtract y from the left member and its equal cx^2 from the right; this leaves

$$\Delta y = 2cx(\Delta x) + c(\Delta x)^2 .$$

The average rate of change of y for this much change in x is

$$\frac{\Delta y}{\Delta x} = 2cx + c(\Delta x) .$$

Hence the derivative of y with respect to x is given by

$$\lim_{\Delta x \to 0} \frac{\Delta y}{\Delta x} = \lim_{\Delta x \to 0} [2cx + c(\Delta x)] = 2cx ,$$

since, when we substitute $\Delta x = 0$, the term $c(\Delta x)$ disappears. We write the result as a formula

$$D_x y = D_x(cx^2) = 2cx .$$

Let $c = 1$ and we have

$$D_x(x^2) = 2x .$$

Thus the derivative with respect to x of the function x^2 is $2x$, while the derivative with respect to x of a constant times x^2 (cx^2) is equal to the

---

* When the motion described by $s = F(t)$ takes place in a straight line, the derivative $D_t s$ gives the direction of motion as well as the speed; i.e., it gives the *velocity*. But when the motion is on a curve, the derivative cannot give the direction; hence it does not give the (vector) velocity.

constant times the derivative of x^2 (c times $2x = 2cx$). This is an instance of a *general law* which states that *the derivative with respect to x of a constant times a function of x is equal to the constant times the derivative with respect to x of the function.**

We can now write $D_x(5x^2) = 10x$; $D_x(-x^2) = -2x$; $D_x(8x^2) = 16x$; $D_x(-4x^2) = -8x$; $D_x(\frac{1}{2}gt^2) = gt$; etc.

The last derivative gives the velocity at the time t of a freely falling body.

6. Differentiation of x^3. Let $y = x^3$, then

$$y + \Delta y = (x + \Delta x)^3 = x^3 + 3x^2(\Delta x) + 3x(\Delta x)^2 + (\Delta x)^3 ,$$

$$\Delta y = 3x^2(\Delta x) + 3x(\Delta x)^2 + (\Delta x)^3 ,$$

$$\frac{\Delta y}{\Delta x} = 3x^2 + 3x(\Delta x) + (\Delta x)^2 ,$$

$$D_x y = D_x(x^3) = 3x^2 .$$

Using the last result and the general law, we can write $D_x(4x^3) = 4D_x(x^3) = 12x^2$; $D_x(-2x^3) = -6x^2$; $D_x(7x^3) = 21x^2$; etc.

Consider, now, the function $y = x^3 + x^2$, then $y + \Delta y = (x + \Delta x)^3 + (x + \Delta x)^2$. On the right appear all of the terms which were on the right in the last problem plus all of the terms which were on the right of the corresponding equation in section 5 (for $c = 1$). The reader can easily verify that when the binomials are expanded and the average change is computed, it will be

$$\frac{\Delta y}{\Delta x} = 3x^2 + 3x(\Delta x) + (\Delta x)^2 + 2x + (\Delta x) ,$$

hence

$$D_x y = D_x(x^3 + x^2) = D_x x^3 + D_x x^2 = 3x^2 + 2x .$$

This is an instance of a *second general law* which states that *the derivative of the sum of two functions is equal to the sum of the derivatives.* More generally, the x-derivative of the algebraic sum of a finite number of functions of x is equal to the algebraic sum of their x-derivatives.

Thus, $D_x(2x^3 - 7x^2) = 6x^2 - 14x$; $D_x(-4x^3 + 3x^2) = -12x^2 + 6x$; $D_x(2x^2 - 7x) = 4x - 7$; etc.

7. Differentiation of x^n. Let $y = x^n$ where n is any given positive integer. Then

$$y + \Delta y = (x + \Delta x)^n = x^n + nx^{n-1}(\Delta x) + \cdots ,$$

---

* See Logsdon, *Elementary Mathematical Analysis*, I, 131, for proof of the general law.

where the continuation dots indicate that there are terms, if n is greater than 1, containing $(\Delta x)^2$, $(\Delta x)^3$, and every power of Δx up to and including $(\Delta x)^n$. Subtracting y and dividing by Δx as usual, we get

$$\frac{\Delta y}{\Delta x} = nx^{n-1} + \cdots ,$$

where every term not written down has Δx as a factor at least once. When Δx is replaced by zero, all of the terms not written down become zero and there is left merely

$$D_x y = D_x (x^n) = nx^{n-1} .$$

This formula is called the **power formula** because it gives at sight the derivative of a positive integral power of x. It is valid for $n=1$ and becomes

$$D_x x = 1 ,$$

i.e., *the derivative of a variable with respect to itself is unity.* It is easy to prove the last formula by adding an increment to x, etc., instead of merely substituting $n=1$ in the power formula.

We can now write $D_x(x^5) = 5x^4$; $D_x(2x^7) = 14x^6$; $D_x(x^4 - 2x^2 + 6x) = 4x^3 - 4x + 6$; etc.

As a matter of fact, the power formula holds for *any real value of n,* whether the value be negative or fractional or even irrational. We shall not attempt to prove this statement for a general n, but shall show that it is correct for $n = -1$ by computing directly the derivative of $y = 1/x$. (By definition,* $x^{-1} = 1/x$). We have

$$y + \Delta y = \frac{1}{x + \Delta x} ,$$

$$\Delta y = \frac{1}{x + \Delta x} - \frac{1}{x} ,$$

$$\Delta y = \frac{-\Delta x}{x(x + \Delta x)} ,$$

$$\frac{\Delta y}{\Delta x} = \frac{-1}{x(x + \Delta x)} ,$$

$$D_x y = \frac{-1}{x^2} .$$

* The meaning of negative exponents is discussed in appendix B, p. 180.

Now since, by definition, $x^{-2} = 1/x^2$, we write $D_x x^{-1} = -x^{-2}$, which is exactly what comes from the power formula when n is set equal to -1.

We may now write $D_x \sqrt{x} = D_x(x^{\frac{1}{2}}) = \frac{1}{2}x^{-\frac{1}{2}} = \dfrac{1}{2\sqrt{x}}$; $D_x(5x^{\frac{3}{4}}) = \frac{15}{4}x^{-\frac{1}{4}}$; $D_x(4x^4 - 2x^2$ $-5x + 1/x^2 - 9/x^3) = 16x^3 - 4x - 5 - 2x^{-3} + 27x^{-4}$.

The power formula is a very useful one, inasmuch as a large number of the functions which express relations in everyday life are given in terms of powers of an unknown. The reader should not fail to note that, although limits were used to obtain the power formula, it can be used without any knowledge of them.

8. Differentiation of a constant. Let $y = c$ where c is any real number. Then $y + \Delta y = c$, $\Delta y = 0$, $\Delta y / \Delta x = 0$, and finally* $D_x y = D_x c = 0$, i.e., *the derivative of a constant is zero.* This is not to be confused with the derivative of a constant times a function given in section 5.

Thus, $D_x(8x^2 + 7) = 16x$; $D_x(2x^5 - 7x + 11 - 2/x) = 10x^4 - 7 + 2/x^2$.

9. Use of the derivative in constructing graphs. It is now possible to make an application of the notion of the derivative to practical problems of everyday life, and the next three sections are devoted to this. The type of problem solved (they are called problems in **maxima and minima**) is of the highest importance. Simple geometrical problems of this type are discussed first. They are followed by a number of "story" problems which, it is hoped, will give to the reader an idea of the scope of application of this theory and of its commercial, as well as theoretical, importance. These problems cannot be solved without use of the derivative.

In the preceding sections we have been studying the technique of differentiating certain types of functions. This has all been done by purely algebraic processes, and it is high time that we call upon our analytical geometry to see what geometrical significance these processes have. Let the curve in the next figure be the graph of a function of x, $y = f(x)$. On an arc which is rising, mark a point $P(x, y)$. On the same rising arc take a point Q near P and lying to the right of P. The abscissa of Q can be denoted by

---

* The function $y = c$ may be written $y = cx^\circ$ (see p. 181). In this form the power formula shows $D_x y = D_x cx^\circ = 0$, as above.

$x+\Delta x$ where Δx is positive. Likewise, the ordinate of Q can be denoted by $y+\Delta y$ and Δy *is also positive;* it is $R'Q$ in the figure.

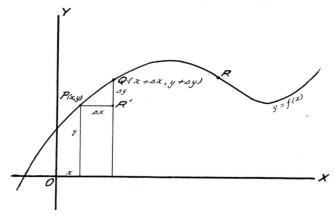

A value of Δx smaller than the one in the figure corresponds to a new position of Q nearer to P and likewise a new value of $R'Q=\Delta y$; but regardless of how small the value of Δx is taken, as long as Δx is positive, the same is true of Δy and the quotient $\Delta y/\Delta x$ is a positive number.

If, on the other hand, Δx were given a negative value, but always so that the point Q is on the rising arc, Q would lie to the left of P and Δy would also be negative ($y+\Delta y$, the ordinate of Q, would be less than y, the ordinate of P). In this case also, $\Delta y/\Delta x$ is a *positive* number. Hence, when the limiting value of $\Delta y/\Delta x$ as Δx approaches zero is found (by some algebraic process), *it will be found to be positive at the point* P, i.e., at any point on a rising arc. *When the curve is rising, the derivative is positive. When the curve is falling, the derivative is negative.* This is seen by taking $P(x, y)$ and $Q(x+\Delta x, y+\Delta y)$ on a falling arc. When Δx is positive, Δy is negative; and when Δx is negative, Δy is positive. The reader should draw a figure and verify for himself these statements.

Consider now an arc, e.g., the arc PQR in the last figure, which rises to a maximum point and then begins to fall. To the left of the maximum point the derivative is positive, but it is decreasing as x increases, since the curve rises less slowly as it approaches the highest point; to the right of the maximum point the derivative is negative, starting with a very small negative value and becoming larger numerically, as evidenced by the fact that the arc falls more and more rapidly as x increases; at the maximum point the curve ceases rising and begins falling, and hence the derivative ceases being positive and begins being negative. It is provable that *at a maximum point the derivative is zero*, and, likewise, *at a minimum point the derivative is zero.**

The last statement suggests a method for finding the maximum and minimum points of a graph. This method is as follows: (*a*) *Find the derivative of the function whose graph is being investigated;* (*b*) *set the derivative equal to zero;* (*c*) *find the roots of the equation thus obtained,* viz., the equation

$$D_x y = 0 .$$

The roots are called **critical values of** x since they are abscissas of points on the curve which are very special points; let us call them **critical points.** Now, if there are maximum points or if there are minimum points, *their abscissas are found among the critical values of* x. The next step then is: (*d*) *Find the ordinates of all the points* whose abscissas have been obtained in this manner, and include all of these points in the table of points which are to be plotted. It is generally easy to determine whether a point obtained in this way is a maximum point or a minimum point, or is neither a maximum nor a minimum point.

A never failing test is to examine the derivative at a point on the left of the critical point and near it, and at another point on the right of the critical point and near it. If the respective signs (algebraic signs of the numbers thus computed) are $+$, $-$, the critical point is a maximum point; if they are $-$, $+$, the critical point is a minimum point; if they are $+$, $+$, or $-$, $-$, the critical point is neither a maximum point nor a minimum point.

Numerous examples will be given.

10. Graphs of linear functions. The theory developed in the last section can be applied very easily to linear functions. The result is simple indeed since a linear function does not have either a maximum point or a minimum point. We start with the general linear function

$$y = ax + b .$$

---

* The derivative cannot be positive here, or else the curve would continue to rise; it cannot be negative at this point, or else the ordinate would be less than the ordinates to the left and very near.

DISCUSSION. The derivative of y with respect to x is equal to

$$D_x(ax+b) = a .$$

This is *constant;* hence does not change its value when x changes. This means that the rate of change of the function $ax+b$ is constant (uni-

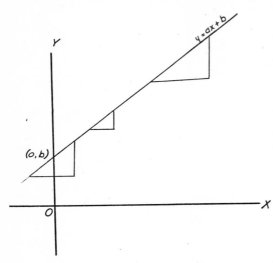

form); or, stated in other words, no matter what point of the graph is under consideration (see the accompanying figure), a given change in x causes a change of a times as much in y. The straight line is the only geometrical figure which has this property; hence we can say that *the graph of a linear function is a straight line* which is rising (as x increases) when a is a positive number, is falling when a is a negative number, and is horizontal when a is zero.

The point $(0, b)$ is a point of the graph, as can be seen by substituting $x=0$ and $y=b$ simultaneously. The point $(0, b)$ lies on the y-axis, and the number b is called the **y-intercept** of the line. As many other points on the line may be found as are desired; we need merely to give to x any arbitrary value and compute the corresponding value of y. When the y-intercept and one additional point are plotted or when any two convenient points are computed and plotted, the line determined by them may be drawn.

Consider, now, the linear functions $y=3x+7$, $y=3x+2$, and $y=3x-4$. For each of these functions the derivative is 3; hence y increases three times as fast as x increases. The graphs of the functions are three *parallel* lines which cut the y-axis 7 units above the origin, 2 units above the origin, and 4 units below the origin, respectively. These and other linear graphs are shown in the figures.

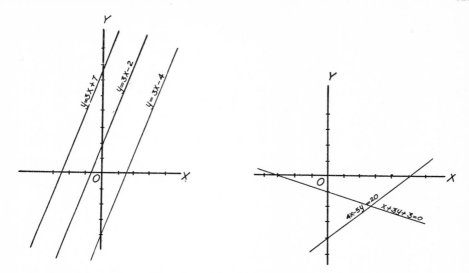

A well-known linear relationship is that between *temperature expressed in degrees Centigrade and in degrees Fahrenheit.* Let C and F designate the temperature on the respective scales. Then the equation

$$C = \tfrac{5}{9}(F-32)$$

expresses C as a function of F. Any F-temperature is converted into its equivalent C-temperature by merely substituting for F in the right member; e.g., when $F = 32°$, $C = 0°$; when $F = 212°$, $C = 100°$; when $F = 95°$, $C = 35°$; etc. The derivative of C with respect to F is 5/9; hence C changes uniformly with F. The reader should make a graph of this relationship.

A second well-known linear relationship expresses the *interest on a*

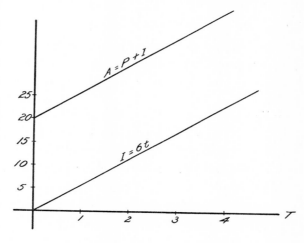

fixed sum P at a fixed rate r for a variable number of years. Let t be the time in years and, say, take $P = \$100$ and $r = 6$ per cent, then the interest, I, is given by

$$I = 6t ;$$

and we have

$$D_t I = 6 ,$$

an equation which shows that the interest increases uniformly with the time.

When the interest is *not compounded*, the amount due is a linear function of the time; in the example given it is

$$A = 6t + 100 ;$$

but when the interest is compounded one or more times each year, the formula which gives the amount as a function of the time is much more

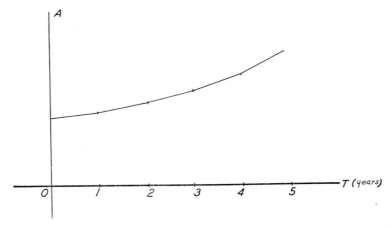

complicated. Its graph consists of broken lines, as in the figure. At the end of each year (if compounded annually) the rate of change increases suddenly, since the interest is now to be computed on a larger sum than the year before. (In the figure the changes in the directions of the lines are exaggerated for emphasis. They correspond more nearly to a 20 per cent interest than a legal 6 per cent.)

The formula $v = at$ shows that velocity is here a uniform function of the time. We have $D_t v = a$. Hence, every second the velocity increases

a units per second. This is the case of a body which starts to move from rest at $t=0$. If at $t=0$, it had already acquired a velocity of v_0 units per second, its velocity at the end of t seconds is given by

$$v=v_0+at .$$

Here, again, the derivative with respect to the time is the constant a, showing that the velocity increases uniformly with the time.

11. Graphs of quadratic functions. The discussion of the graphs of quadratic functions will be given in several steps, starting with the simple quadratic function

$$y=ax^2 , \qquad (a\neq0) .$$

We first compute $D_x y = D_x(ax^2) = 2ax$. This expression depends on x, from which we conclude that the rate of change of the function x^2 is *not constant*, as was the case with the function $ax+b$. The derivative is zero when $x=0$, and for no other value of x except $x=0$. We wish to ascertain whether the critical value $x=0$ is the abscissa of a turning-point of the graph of the function and, if so, whether the turning-point is a maximum point or a minimum point. There are two cases according as the coefficient a is positive or negative.

(1) *Let a be positive.* Then, when x is less than zero but not much less, the derivative $2ax$ is negative but small in numerical value; while, when x is greater than zero but not much greater, the derivative is positive but small in value. This means that the curve is falling as x increases toward zero (going from left to right), while it is rising as x continues on beyond zero, still going in the direction of increasing abscissas. Hence the point whose abscissa is zero is a *minimum* point on the curve. The next figure shows graphs of $y=ax^2$ for $a=1$, $a=3$, and $a=\frac{1}{2}$.

(2) *Let a be negative.* Then, when x changes from large negative values to smaller negative values, then to zero, and finally to larger and larger positive values, the derivative $2ax$ changes from large positive values to smaller positive values, is then zero, and finally takes larger and larger negative values. The point $(0, 0)$ is now a *maximum* point. In the figure are shown graphs of $y=-2x^2$ and of $y=-\frac{1}{2}x^2$, each of which has

a maximum at the origin. When a is positive, the graphs are **concave upward**; otherwise they are concave downward.

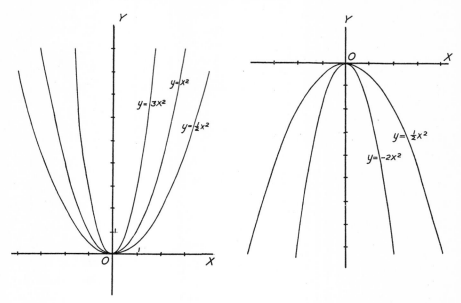

The name given to the graph of ax^2 is **parabola**. The turning-point is called the **vertex** of the parabola. The vertical line drawn through the vertex is an **axis of symmetry** of the parabola. It divides the parabola into two equal parts so placed that, if the sheet of paper were folded on the axis of symmetry, the two parts of the graph would coincide.

Note. Every diameter of a circle is an axis of symmetry; but an ellipse has only two axes of symmetry, though every diameter of an ellipse divides it into two equal parts. An isosceles triangle has one axis of symmetry, but an equilateral triangle has three axes of symmetry.

To make the graph of a quadratic function, a parabola, the most important thing is to be able to find the abscissa and ordinate of the vertex. When this point is plotted and the axis drawn through it, it is only necessary to compute a few more points in order to get a picture of the relationship expressed by the equation. When a point is computed and plotted, the symmetric point can be marked off without additional computation.

EXAMPLE. Construct and discuss the graph of the quadratic function

$$y = ax^2 + c .$$

DISCUSSION. The derivative is again $2ax$; hence the argument regarding changes in the derivative need not be repeated. The conclusion is that the graph of this function also is concave upward when a is a positive number; otherwise it is concave downward. The abscissa of the vertex, found by solving the equation $2ax = 0$, is again $x = 0$, but the ordinate of the vertex is now $y = c$. Suppose that a table of values had been computed for, say, $y = x^2$; and consider now a table of values for $y = x^2 + c$, say $x^2 + 3$. If the entries in the x-columns of the two tables are the same, corresponding entries in the y-columns differ by 3 units. This means that the graph of the latter can be obtained from the graph of the former by cutting out a pattern of the former and moving it 3 units upward. More generally, the graph of $y = x^2 + c$ can be obtained by moving the pattern for $y = x^2$ up c units if c is positive or down c units if c is negative. The next figures show graphs of $y = x^2 + 2$, $y = x^2 - 1$, $y = x^2 - 5$, $y = -\frac{1}{2}x^2 - 3$, $y = -\frac{1}{2}x^2 + 3$, and $y = -\frac{1}{2}x^2 - 1$.

x	$y = x^2$	x	$y = x^2 + 3$
0	0	0	3
1	1	1	4
2	4	2	7
3	9	3	12
4	16	4	19
-1	1	-1	4
-2	4	-2	7

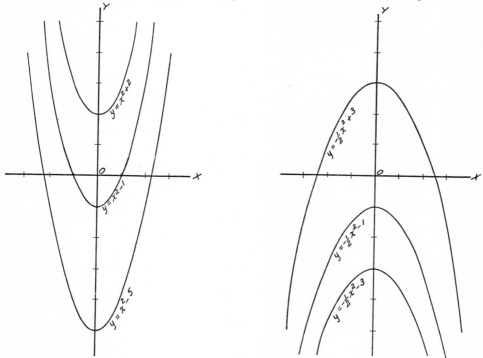

We may now say that the equation $y = x^2 + c$, where c may take any real value, is the equation of all the parabolas in the plane which may be obtained by tracing around the pattern of the parabola $y = x^2$ when the pattern is placed so that its axis coincides with the y-axis. These parabolas are called **unit parabolas.** Furthermore, the equation $y = ax^2 + c$ is the equation of all the parabolas in the plane which have the y-axis as an axis of symmetry.

EXAMPLE. Construct and discuss the graph of the quadratic function

$$y = ax^2 + bx + c .$$

DISCUSSION. The derivative is $2ax + b$. This is zero* when $x = -b/2a$. For a positive, the derivative is negative when x is less than $-b/2a$, and it is positive for x greater

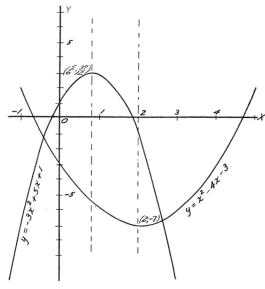

than $-b/2a$. Hence the abscissa of the vertex is $-b/2a$ and the ordinate is obtained by substituting $-b/2a$ for x in the given function. The axis of symmetry is the vertical line through the vertex; its equation is $x = -b/2a$. The parabola is concave upward.

For a negative, the parabola is concave downward and the axis of the parabola is again the line $x = -b/2a$.

In the figure are two parabolas, graphs of quadratic functions. The discussions which follow the graphs exhibit the importance of the derivative in constructing even simple graphs.

For the graph of the function $y = x^2 - 4x - 3$, we can say
   $a)$ The derivative of the function is $2x - 4$;
   $b)$ The derivative is zero when $x = 2$;
   $c)$ The vertex is the point $(2, -7)$;
   $d)$ The axis is the line $x = 2$;
   $e)$ The parabola is concave upward.
For the graph of the function $y = -3x^2 + 5x + 1$, we can say
   $a)$ The derivative of the function is $-6x + 5$;
   $b)$ The derivative is zero when $x = 5/6$;
   $c)$ The vertex is the point $(5/6, 37/12)$;
   $d)$ The axis is the line $x = 5/6$;
   $e)$ The parabola is concave downward.

* Set $2ax + b = 0$; then $2ax = -b$, $x = -b/2a$. Now assume that a is positive and set $x = k$, where k is less than $-b/2a$. Then $D_x y = 2ak + b$, a negative number as asserted above.

You should be able to obtain the corresponding items of information and construct the graphs of the quadratic functions

(i) $y = 2x^2 + 6x$,   (ii) $y = \frac{1}{2}x^2 - 4x + 1$,   (iii) $y = \frac{1}{4}x^2 + x - 2$.

12. Graphs of polynomial functions. A polynomial function is a function $y = $ *function of* x, or $y = f(x)$, where on the right of the equality sign is a *polynomial* in x. The simplest polynomial is the linear function $ax + b$, which has already been discussed. The polynomial of next highest degree is the quadratic, whose graph is the parabola studied in the last section. It is not necessary to make a study of cubic functions, quartic functions, quintic functions, etc., separately, since many of the properties of the one are also properties of the others. Let us use n as a symbol for the degree of the polynomial function to be considered, then certain general remarks can be made, as follows:

a) A polynomial function of x is a single-valued function of x, i.e., for a given arbitrary real value of x there is a single real value of y. Geometrically, this means that every vertical line ($x = $ constant) cuts the graph in one and only one point.

b) The graph is a continuous curve. This seems intuitive from (*a*) and the fact that a very small change in x causes a very small change in y. We shall not attempt to make a proof of this property.

c) The degree of the derivative is $n - 1$, since differentiating a power of x reduces the degree by one unit. An equation of degree $n - 1$ has exactly $n - 1$ roots. If all of these roots are real and different, the graph has $n - 1$ real turning-points; otherwise it has fewer than $n - 1$ real turning-points.

d) To make a graph of a polynomial function, we need to *find the abscissas of the turning-points*, then make a table of points which includes all of the turning-points and as many more points as are needed in order to get the desired accuracy. Generally in the table should be included, in addition to the turning-points, one or two points between each pair of consecutive turning-points, one or two points before the first turn, and one or two points after the last turn. This will be illustrated in the following examples.

EXAMPLE 1. Construct the graph of the function

$$y = x^3 + 4x^2 - 10 .$$

DISCUSSION. The derivative is $3x^2 + 8x$. When this is set equal to zero, the roots are found to be $x = 0$ and $x = -8/3$. In the table of points we include $x = -4$ and -3 whose values are less than $-8/3$, $x = -2$ and -1, whose values lie between the numbers 0 and $-8/3$, and finally, $x = 1$ and 2, both of which are abscissas of points on the curve lying to the right of the last turning-point. From the table the graph is constructed. It is shown in the figure.

x	-4	-3	$-\frac{8}{3}$	-2	-1	0	1	2
y	-10	-1	$-\frac{14}{27}$	-2	-7	-10	-5	14

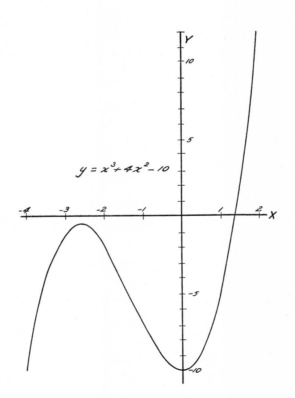

EXAMPLE 2. Construct the graph of the function $y = x^3 - 1$.

DISCUSSION. The derivative, $3x^2$, when set equal to zero gives only $x = 0$ as a possible turning-point. In the table of points we include $x = -2, -1, 0, 1,$ and 2, and compute the corresponding ordinates.

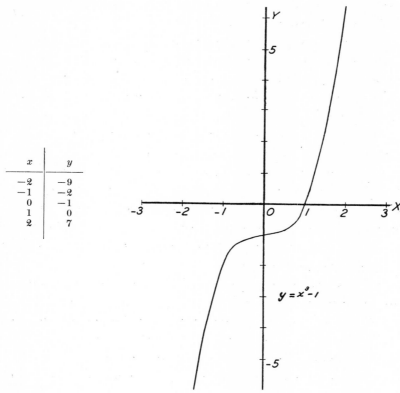

x	y
-2	-9
-1	-2
0	-1
1	0
2	7

$$y = x^3 - 1$$

The graph shows that the curve has no turning-point. The derivative also gives this information, for, since $3x^2$ is always positive, the curve is always rising. The reader will note that it has never been stated that each root of the equation

$$D_x y = 0$$

is the abscissa of a turning-point. The statement was (p. 119) that *the abscissas of all the turning-points are found* **among** *the roots of the derivative equation*. This example shows that among the roots of the derivative equation may be abscissas of points which are not turning-points.

13. Practical applications of maxima and minima. The preceding sections have been quite formal in type. They were designed to prepare the way for a series of applications of the calculus to everyday problems—applications whose scope and importance cannot fail to fill the mind with amazement and admiration.

Stated briefly, we have been trying to show that, by the use of the derivative, the maximum value or values and the minimum value or values of functions which possess maximum values or minimum values can be found. In everyday life, problems requiring the determination of maxima and minima of functions are frequently encountered. These problems are generally comparatively simple to treat, inasmuch as the functions arising often have only one maximum value or one minimum value. As examples, cylindrical storage tanks for oil are to be built, or a cistern is to be dug and lined with cement, or cans for fruit are to be cut out of tin. In each of these cases the capacity of the container is fixed in advance; and it is important to be able to ascertain the most favorable dimensions, i.e., the shape of the container which will require the least material or whose construction will cost least.

Again, assuming that the strength of a rectangular beam placed in a horizontal position is proportional to the product of the breadth and the square of the depth of a cross-section, it is required to find the breadth and depth of the strongest rectangular beam which can be cut from a cylindrical log, the diameter of whose cross-section is d inches.

Other problems involving maxima and minima may deal with the position of a source of light in order to obtain maximum illumination of a given area; with the most efficient speed for a given automobile or steamboat; with the greatest possible range of a projectile shot from a cannon with a given muzzle velocity; in fact, it is not possible to complete an enumeration of the kinds of problems that can be solved by use of the theory which has been developed regarding maxima and minima. Some of these problems will now be stated and solved.

EXAMPLE 1. It is desired to make a box out of a square sheet of metal k inches in length by cutting out squares from the corners and turning up the sides. Find the dimensions of the largest box which can be made in this manner.

SOLUTION. Let the side of the square to be cut out be denoted by x. Then the volume, V, of the box is the product of the area of the square base by the altitude x, i.e.,

$$V = x(k-2x)^2 = k^2x - 4kx^2 + 4x^3 .$$

From this we get

$$D_x V = k^2 - 8kx + 12x^2 .$$

To find the critical values of x the derivative is set equal to zero and the resulting equation is solved for x by the quadratic formula, as follows:

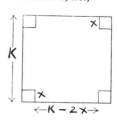

$$12x^2 - 8kx + k^2 = 0 ,$$

$$x = \frac{8k \pm \sqrt{64k^2 - 48k^2}}{24} = \frac{8k \pm 4k}{24} = \tfrac{1}{2}k \qquad \text{or} \qquad \tfrac{1}{6}k .$$

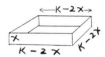

When $x = \tfrac{1}{2}k$, the sheet of metal is entirely cut away and the volume of the box is zero. This answer has no meaning, inasmuch as it does not satisfy the conditions of the problem.

When $x = \tfrac{1}{6}k$, $V = x(k-2x)^2 = \tfrac{2}{27}k^3$. In order to ascertain whether or not this is really a maximum value, we examine the derivative, $k^2 - 8kx + 12x^2$, for a value of x less than $\tfrac{1}{6}k$ and for a value of x which lies between $\tfrac{1}{6}k$ and $\tfrac{1}{2}k$. We find that for $x = \tfrac{1}{12}k$, $D_x V = \tfrac{5}{12}k^2$, a *positive* number, while for $x = \tfrac{1}{4}k$, $D_x V = -\tfrac{1}{4}k^2$, a *negative* number. Hence, $\tfrac{2}{27}k^3$ is truly the greatest volume which can be secured in the manner described.

EXAMPLE 2. Two roads which intersect at right angles bound two sides of X's farm. There is a sulphur well 10 rods from one road and 20 rods from the other. In order to make

the well accessible to passing travelers, it is proposed to build a driveway from one of the present roads to the other skirting the well. How shall the driveway be run in order that the area of the triangular part of X's farm which is cut off shall be the least possible?

SOLUTION. Let the relative positions of the well, W, and the intersecting roads be as indicated in the figure; let EB be the outer boundary of the triangle to be cut off; and let $CB = x$. Then from similar triangles we can write

$$\frac{DE}{20} = \frac{10}{x} ,$$

$$DE = \frac{200}{x} .$$

The area of the triangle BFE is given by

$$A = \tfrac{1}{2}(FB)(FE),$$

$$A = \tfrac{1}{2}(20+x)\left(10+\frac{200}{x}\right),$$

$$A = \frac{1}{2}\left(400+10x+\frac{4,000}{x}\right),$$

$$A = 200+5x+\frac{2,000}{x}.$$

Hence

$$D_x A = 5 - \frac{2,000}{x^2}.$$

The value of $D_x A$ is zero when $5x^2 = 2,000$, i.e., when $x^2 = 400$; hence $x = 20$. But when $x = 20$ rods, $A = 400$ sq. rd.

To show that this is truly a minimum value for A, we must show that $D_x A$ is *negative* for a value less than 20 but not much less, and is *positive* for a value of x greater than 20 but not much greater. We try 19 and 21. For $x = 19$, $D_x A$ has the value $-195/361$, while for $x = 21$, $D_x A$ has the value $205/441$. Hence the road starts 20 rods from C, as indicated in the drawing.

EXAMPLE 3. A farmer who purchased 1,200 ft. of metal fencing from the Century of Progress Exposition desires to inclose a rectangular cattle lot by fencing three sides and

using a fence already in place for the fourth side. What is the greatest area which he can inclose?

SOLUTION. Let x be the width of his lot and $1,200-2x$ its length. Then

$$A = 1,200x - 2x^2,$$

$$D_x A = 1,200 - 4x.$$

The derivative is zero when $x = 300$. Then the length of the lot is 600, and its area is 180,000 sq. ft., approximately 1 acre and 21 sq. rd.

To show that this is a maximum, we set $x = 280$ and 320 in turn in the derivative. The respective values of $D_x A$ are positive, negative. Hence the value $x = 300$ corresponds to a maximum value of the area.

EXAMPLE 4. What is the largest rectangle which can be cut out of a given circular sheet of metal?

SOLUTION. Let r denote the known radius of the circle and x the unknown length of the rectangle. Then (cf. the figure) the width of the rectangle is $\sqrt{4r^2-x^2}$, and the area is given by

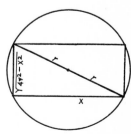

$$A = x\sqrt{4r^2-x^2},$$

$$A = \sqrt{4r^2 x^2 - x^4}.$$

In order that we may avoid having to differentiate the radical expression which is the value of A, we can make use of the fact that any values of x which makes $\sqrt{4r^2x^2-x^4}$ a maximum will also make the function $4r^2x^2-x^4$ a maximum. Thus we deal with the function

$$B=4r^2x^2-x^4 .$$

Then

$$D_x B=8r^2x-4x^3 ,$$

and the right member is zero for $x=0$ and for $x=r\sqrt{2}$.

When $x=0$, the area of the rectangle is zero; when $x=r\sqrt{2}$, the width of the rectangle is also $r\sqrt{2}$, i.e., the rectangle is a square whose area is $2r^2$. We cannot aver that this is a maximum without investigating the derivative, say for $x=r$ and for $x=\frac{3}{2}r$. The investigation can be made for $D_x B$ instead of $D_x A$. We get $D_x B$, for $x=r$ has the value $4r^3$, a *positive* number; while its value for $x=\frac{3}{2}r$ is $-\frac{3}{2}r^3$, a *negative* number. Hence, both of the functions, B and A, have maximum values for $x=r\sqrt{2}$.

EXAMPLE 5. The distance from the earth of a ball shot upward with an initial velocity of 1,000 ft./sec. is given by

$$s=1,000t-16.1t^2 .$$

How high does the ball rise?

SOLUTION. The velocity of the ball is expressed by

$$D_t s=1,000-32.2t ,$$

and the distance is a maximum when $D_t s=0$, i.e., when $t=1,000/32.2=15,528$ ft. = (approx.) 2.9 mi.

CHAPTER 7

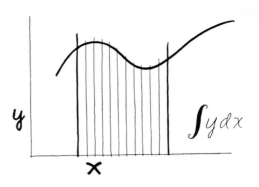

THE INTEGRAL CALCULUS

BEFORE beginning the study of the integral calculus, let us review what we have found out about the differential calculus. We have seen that it deals with the process of finding derivatives and of making use of derivatives in the solution of problems. In this book applications to maxima and minima are made. Other applications, the theory and use of which are discussed in calculus texts, are:

a) The slope of a curve at a given point,
b) The tangent to a curve at a given point,
c) The angle at which two curves intersect,
d) The order of contact of two curves,
e) The curvature of a curve at a given point,
f) Singular points of a curve,
g) Multiple roots of an algebraic equation,
h) Small errors and corrections, relative errors.

This tabulation of properties of a *function which is changing* or of the graph of such a function is far from complete. A proper study and understanding of them is not possible without a knowledge of derivatives.

When, instead of a changing function, we consider a moving object which moves in accordance with a known or an assumed law of motion, the scope of application of the derivative is the entire field of mechanics, viz., dynamics of a particle, statics, thermodynamics, the construction and operation of machines, engineering, celestial mechanics, relativity, etc. It is no exaggeration to say that the field of application of the derivative is the universe.

What a vast scope for the use of the idea of *finding a limiting value to the quotient which is obtained by dividing the increment of a function by the corresponding increment of its independent variable.*

The *underlying notion of the* **integral calculus** is also that of *finding a limiting value,* but this time it is the limiting value of a sum of terms when the number of terms increases without bound at the same time that the numerical value of each term approaches zero. The area bounded by one or more curves is found as the limiting value of a sum of small rectangles; the length of an arc of a curve is found as the limiting value of a sum of lengths of straight lines (chords of the arc); the volume of a solid bounded by one or more curved surfaces is found as the limiting value of a sum of volumes of small solids bounded by planes; etc. In discussing examples illustrating the use of this notion, it is not possible here to go into detail as to the analytic properties of curves which may be used as boundaries or whose lengths may be computed. Suffice it to say that all of the curves which here appear have been carefully chosen so as to present no insuperable difficulties. It is also true that the theory has been so refined that the mathematician can ascertain with accuracy whether a given problem can or cannot be solved.

1. **The integral as an infinite sum. Plane area.** As a first example in the use of the process called **integration**, let it be required to find the area A bounded by the graph of the function $y = f(x)$, the ordinates $x = a$, $x = b(b > a)$, and the x-axis, the shaded area in the figure on the following page. It is called **the area under the curve from $x = a$ to $x = b$.**

Divide the line segment MN, whose length is $b - a$ units, into n equal parts, where n is any fixed positive integer (in the figure n is 6). Call the points of subdivision $M_1, M_2, \ldots, M_{n-1}$; use the notation Δx to designate the length of each of the sub-intervals, MM_1, M_1M_2, etc.; then the abscissas of $M_1, M_2, \ldots, M_{n-1}$ are, respectively, $x_1 = a + \Delta x$, $x_2 = a + 2\Delta x, \ldots, x_{n-1} = a + (n-1)\Delta x$. At each point M_i, $(i = 1, 2, \ldots, n-1)$, erect the ordinate to the curve and let it meet the curve at P_i. If, for symmetry, we set $a = x_0$ and $f(a) = f(x_0) = y_0$, the lengths of the ordinates are $y_0 = f(x_0)$, $y_1 = f(x_1)$, ... , $y_{n-1} = f(x_{n-1})$.

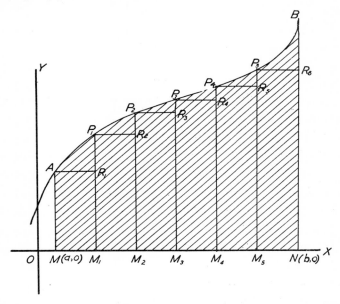

Draw horizontal line segments AR_1, P_1R_2, P_2R_3, ... , $P_{n-1}R_n$ as indicated in the figure. The areas of the rectangles which lie *wholly within* the shaded portion of the figure are given by

$$f(x_0)\Delta x, \qquad f(x_1)\Delta x, \qquad \ldots, \qquad f(x_{n-1})\Delta x,$$

and their sum is

$$f(x_0)\Delta x + f(x_1)\Delta x + \cdots + f(x_{n-1})\Delta x,$$

a sum which may, for convenience, be indicated by

$$S = \sum_{i=0}^{n-1} f(x_i)\Delta x \qquad (a \leq x_i < b),$$

where the symbol $\sum$ (Greek letter, sigma) is a symbol frequently used to indicate a sum.

Now the sum of the rectangles is less than the shaded area A which we started out to find; indeed, the difference between the two areas is the sum of the small pieces AR_1P_1, $P_1R_2P_2$, etc.

Let n be increased, say doubled or trebled or quadrupled; let all of the new ordinates be drawn; and consider again the sum of all of the rectangles,

$$S = \sum_{i=0}^{n-1} f(x_i)\Delta x, \quad \text{or,} \quad \sum_{i=0}^{n-1} y_i \Delta x, \quad (a \leq x_i < b). \tag{1}$$

We now have an area which is a better approximation to the desired area A than the first sum, and *every time that* n *is increased the sum of the rectangles is a number nearer in value to* A *than before* (since the arc is a rising* arc). Also, by taking n sufficiently large, the error in taking S as the value of A becomes less than any previously assigned number; hence, by the definition of a limit (cf. chap. 6, sec. 3), A is the limit of S as n increases without bound and Δx approaches zero simultaneously. We introduce a new symbol called the **integral sign** or the **sign of integration.** It is the sign of an operation which gives the number obtained when the limiting value of the sum is found (if it exists), while the symbol $\sum$ indicates merely the sum of a *finite* number of terms (an *approximation* for A). Accompanying the $\sum$ symbol is the parenthetical statement which shows that the values of x_i are $\geq a$ and $\leq b$, or, as we may say, the values of x_i *range from a to b*. The letters a and b as used with the definite integral sign have the same meaning. Thus we write, replacing Δx in the finite sum by dx in the infinite sum,

$$A = \int_a^b f(x)dx = \int_a^b ydx = \lim_{\Delta x \to 0} \sum f(x_i)\Delta x.$$

The new symbol is read "the integral from a to b of $f(x)dx$." Even though the algebraic manipulation is rather involved, it seems desirable to give one example solved in the manner described in the paragraph above. In the next section, an easier process of evaluating a definite integral is described.

---

* The argument is the same if the arc is a falling arc. Hence, if an arc is made up of a finite number of rising and falling arcs, the statements are still valid.

EXAMPLE 1. Find the area bounded by the curve whose equation is $y=x^2$, the ordinates $x=a$, $x=b$, and the x-axis.

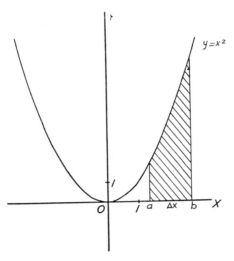

SOLUTION. We have

$$S=[a^2+(a+\Delta x)^2+(a+2\Delta x)^2+ \cdots +\{a+(n-1)\Delta x\}^2]\Delta x$$
$$=[a^2+a^2+2a(\Delta x)+(\Delta x)^2+a^2+4a(\Delta x)+4(\Delta x)^2+a^2+6a(\Delta x)+9(\Delta x)^2+ \cdots$$
$$+a^2+2a(n-1)(\Delta x)+(n-1)^2(\Delta x)^2]\Delta x$$
$$=[na^2+2a(\Delta x)(1+2+3+ \cdots +(n-1))+(1^2+2^2+3^2+$$
$$\cdots +(n-1)^2)(\Delta x)^2]\Delta x$$
$$=n\Delta x[a^2+(n-1)a\Delta x+\tfrac{1}{6}(n+1)(2n+1)(\Delta x)^2]* .$$

$$(2)$$

We shall now replace $n\Delta x$ by its equal $b-a$ and obtain from (1)

$$S=(b-a)[a^2+a(b-a)-a\Delta x+\tfrac{1}{3}(b-a)^2+\tfrac{1}{2}(b-a)\Delta x+\tfrac{1}{6}(\Delta x)^2 .$$

Let Δx approach zero and we get the desired area, viz.,

$$A=(b-a)[a^2+a(b-a)-0+\tfrac{1}{3}(b-a)^2+0+0] ,$$
$$A=(b-a)[a^2+ab-a^2+\tfrac{1}{3}(a^2-2ab+b^2)] ,$$
$$A=(b-a)\left[\frac{b^2+ab+a^2}{3}\right]$$
$$A=\tfrac{1}{3}(b^3-a^3) .$$

* To write equation (2), two formulas which are proved in college algebra texts were used; viz.,

$$1+2+3+ \cdots +(n-1)=\tfrac{1}{2}(n-1)n ,$$
$$1^2+2^2+3^2+ \cdots +(n-1)^2=\tfrac{1}{6}(n+1)n(2n+1) .$$

The solution of the problem above required some algebraic manipulation and the knowledge of two algebraic formulas, one at least of which is not well known. If the function chosen had been less simple than x^2, whether of higher degree or with more terms or both, the algebraic manipulation would have been correspondingly more difficult. Fortunately, the value of an integral of this kind (it is called a **definite integral**), although defined as the limit of an infinite sum, *can be computed by a method far simpler than that of finding a limiting process.* This is really a very remarkable situation, to be able to find the number which is the limit of an infinite sum without recourse to a limiting process. The method is explained in the next paragraph.

2. Anti-derivative. An anti-derivative of $f(x)$ is a function $F(x)$ whose derivative is $f(x)$. For example, the derivative of $7x^4$ is $28x^3$; then an anti-derivative of $28x^3$ is $7x^4$. Other anti-derivatives of $28x^3$ are $7x^4+c$ where c is any real number. Thus every function has an infinite number of anti-derivatives if it has one.

In the last problem, the function which appears under the integral sign is x^2; an anti-derivative of x^2 is $x^3/3$. In this anti-derivative (or any other, say $\dfrac{x^3}{3}+5$ or $\dfrac{x^3}{3}-7$) substitute the numbers b and a, called the **limits of integration**, subtracting* the $a^3/3$ obtained in the one case from the $b^3/3$ obtained in the other. The result is

$$\tfrac{1}{3}(b^3-a^3) \, ,$$

which is precisely the value of $\displaystyle\int_a^b x^2 dx$ found by taking the limit of the sum of the rectangles as Δx approaches zero.

This is an instance of a general theorem proved in all calculus texts and called the **Fundamental Theorem of the Integral Calculus**; viz., the number obtained by substituting and subtracting as described above in

---

* The process described is indicated by $\dfrac{x^3}{3}\bigg]_a^b$, a symbol which is evaluated by the substitutions and subtraction described, viz., $\dfrac{b^3}{3}-\dfrac{a^3}{3}=\dfrac{b^3-a^3}{3}$.

an anti-derivative of $f(x)$ is always equal to the number obtained by finding the limit of the infinite sum (1) as $\Delta x \to 0$. We write

$$\int_a^b f(x)dx = F(b) - F(a) \ ,$$

where $D_x F(x) = f(x)$, and where $f(x)$ is integrable between a and b, i.e., $f(x)$ has the analytic properties which make it possible to operate on it in this way.

To return to the problem in section 1, the area under the curve $y = x^2$ from $x=0$ to $x=3$ is $\frac{1}{3}(3^3 - 0^3) = 9$ square units; the area under the curve from $x = -4$ to $x=5$ is $\frac{1}{3}(125 + 64) = 189/3 = 63$ square units. With the formula available, we can find the area between *any* two ordinates, by simple substitution.

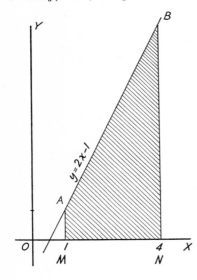

EXAMPLE 2. As a second example, we compute by both methods an area which can also be computed by elementary geometry: To find the area under the curve $y = 2x - 1$ from $x=1$ to $x=4$.

SOLUTION.

a) By elementary geometry the area of the trapezoid $AMNB$ is equal to one-half the sum of the parallel sides multiplied by the altitude. The altitude $MN = 4 - 1 = 3$; the lengths of the parallel sides MA and NB are obtained by substituting $x=1$ and $x=4$, respectively, in the function $y = 2x - 1$; they are 1 and 7. Hence the area is

$$A = \tfrac{1}{2}(1+7)3 = 12 \text{ square units.}$$

b) By use of the definite integral,

$$A = \int_1^4 (2x-1)dx = (x^2 - x) \Big]_1^4 = (4^2 - 4) - (1^2 - 1) = 12 \text{ square units.}$$

c) By finding the limit of an infinite sum, i.e.

$$\lim_{\Delta x \to 0} S = \lim_{\Delta x \to 0} \sum (2x_i - 1)\Delta x \ .$$

To obtain a *general* formula let us form the sum S, using a and b for the end-values of x instead of 1 and 4. We have

$$S = (2a-1)\Delta x + [2(a+\Delta x)-1]\Delta x + [2(a+2\Delta x)-1]\Delta x + \cdots +$$
$$[2(a+(n-1)\Delta x)-1]\Delta x$$
$$= 2a(\Delta x) - \Delta x + 2a(\Delta x) + 2(\Delta x)^2 - \Delta x + 2a(\Delta x) + 4(\Delta x)^2 - \Delta x +$$
$$\cdots + 2a(\Delta x) + 2(n-1)(\Delta x)^2 - \Delta x$$
$$= n(2a(\Delta x)) - n(\Delta x) + 2(\Delta x)^2(1+2+ \cdots +(n-1))$$
$$= 2a(n(\Delta x)) - n(\Delta x) + (\Delta x)^2(n-1)n$$
$$= 2a(b-a) - (b-a) + [n(\Delta x)]^2 - n(\Delta x)^2$$
$$= 2a(b-a) - (b-a) + (b-a)^2 - 0$$
$$= 2ab - 2a^2 - b + a + b^2 - 2ab + a^2$$
$$= (b^2-b) - (a^2-a) .$$

When we set $b=4$ and $a=1$ we get for the area, as before, $16-4-(1-1)=12$ square units.

3. Volume of a solid of revolution. Let the arc AB in the figure be the part of the graph of $y=f(x)$ which corresponds to the values of x from $x=a$ to $x=b(b>a)$ and let the plane figure $MABN$ be revolved about OX. The solid which is generated in this manner is called a *solid of revolution*.

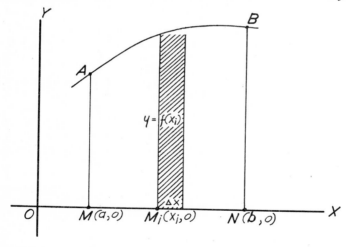

To find its volume, we proceed as follows: Divide the segment MN into a number of equal parts, say n, and denote the length of each part by Δx. At the points of division, erect perpendiculars and draw horizontal line segments, as in the figure on page 136. Lying wholly under the curve AB we now have n rectangles, only one of which is shown in the accompanying figure. As the plane figure $MABN$ revolves about OX, each rectangle generates a solid circular cylinder which has $y_i = f(x_i)$ as the radius of each of its bases and Δx as its altitude. The volume of this cylinder (the area of the base multiplied by the altitude Δx) is $\pi y_i^2 \Delta x$; hence the total volume of the n cylinders can be computed and it is a function of Δx.

By the same argument as was used in discussing plane areas, the volume generated by the arc AB is the limiting value of the sum of the volumes of the cylinders as Δx approaches zero, if there is a limiting value. Again, by the Fundamental Theorem of Integral Calculus, this value can be computed by merely finding an anti-derivative, substituting and subtracting. The reader should not fail to note that this limit, once found, is no longer an approximation to the volume but is its true value.

EXAMPLE 1. Find the volume generated by revolving the arc of the parabola $y = x^2$ from $x = 1$ to $x = 4$ about the x-axis.

SOLUTION. We have $\displaystyle\int_1^4 \pi y^2 dx = \int_1^4 \pi x^4 dx = \pi \left.\frac{x^5}{5}\right]_1^4 = \frac{\pi}{5}(256 - 1) = 51\pi$ cubic units.

EXAMPLE 2. Find the volume of the frustum of a cone generated by revolving about the x-axis the segment of the line $y = 2x - 1$ from $x = 1$ to $x = 4$.

SOLUTION. We have $\displaystyle\int_1^4 \pi y^2 dx = \int_1^4 \pi(2x - 1)^2 dx = \int_1^4 \pi(4x^2 - 4x + 1)dx = \pi(\tfrac{4}{3}x^3 - 2x^2$

$+ x \big]_1^4 = \pi(256/3 - 32 + 4) - \pi(4/3 - 2 + 1) = 57\pi$ cubic units.

This result can be verified by use of the formula for a frustum of a cone which is proved in elementary geometry, viz.: *The volume of a frustum of a right circular cone is one third of the product of its altitude by the number which is the sum of the two bases plus the square root of their product.*

4. Other applications of the definite integral. In a similar manner, in order to find the **length of an arc**, say the arc of $y = f(x)$, from $x = a$ to $x = b$ we divide the line segment MN into n equal parts, erect perpendiculars cutting the arc AB in $P_1, P_2, \ldots, P_{n-1}$, join $AP_1, P_1P_2, \ldots, P_{n-1}B$ by line segments, and compute the sum S of the lengths of these chords as a function of n and Δx. The length of the arc AB is the limit of S as $n \to \infty$ and $\Delta x \to 0$ simultaneously.

To find the **area of the surface of revolution** generated by revolving the arc AB in the figure about OX, we find the area of the frustum of a cone generated by one of the chords P_iP_{i+1}, then find S the sum of the n

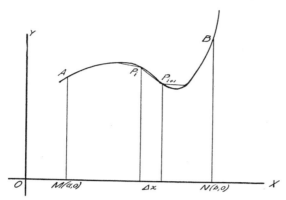

areas generated by the n chords. The area of the surface of revolution is the limit of S as $n \to \infty$ and $\Delta x \to 0$ simultaneously.

For example, the figure obtained by revolving a parabola about its axis is called a *paraboloid of revolution*. The mirror of a reflecting telescope has the shape of a paraboloid of revolution. If the cost of silvering 1 square unit of surface is known, the total cost of silvering, say, the 100-inch reflector at Mount Wilson, can be computed after the total area has been obtained by the method described above.

It is not possible to compute the areas of curved surfaces, the lengths of curved lines, or volumes bounded by curved surfaces by any method other than the two methods described in this chapter, viz., (1) the actual use of the limiting process, and (2) the definite integral, computed by the use of an anti-derivative as justified by the Fundamental Theorem of the Integral Calculus.

Another interesting application of the use of the definite integral is in computing fluid pressure. An engineer, when about to construct a dam, needs to know the amount of pressure which each portion of the dam must withstand; and since the pressure increases with the depth, he increases the thickness of his dam with the depth. The following discussion shows how he can obtain the information which he needs.

Take the x-axis on the surface of the water, and consider the pressure on a narrow strip of the wall bounded by the horizontal lines in the figure.

The top of this strip is y units below the surface of the water, and the bottom is $y+\Delta y$ units below it. At any point the pressure is equal in all directions;* hence we can obtain an approximation of the pressure on this strip by computing the pressure on a *horizontal* strip of equal dimensions which is y units below the surface. The latter number is easily determined. It is merely the weight of the column of water supported by the strip. To find the weight, we multiply the volume in any convenient cubic units by the weight of 1 cubic unit of water. The volume is equal to the volume of a column of water whose height is y units, whose thickness is Δy units, and whose width is the width of the stream which is to be dammed.

When the pressure on one narrow strip is computed in this manner as a function of y and Δy, we

Engineer at work

have merely to find the definite integral of this function as y varies from $y=0$ (the surface of the water) to $y=$ the height of the dam.

In the next tabulation are listed the cases already discussed, together with the more common of other types of problems in which it is desired to discover the values of quantities whose determination resolves itself into the computation of one or more infinite sums of this character, and whose computation, therefore, because of the Fundamental Theorem of Integral Calculus, requires only the evaluation of a definite integral. They are

a) Plane area
b) Length of arc
c) Area of a surface of revolution
d) Volume of a solid of revolution
e) Fluid pressure
f) Center of fluid pressure

g) Center of gravity
h) Center of mass
i) Moment of inertia
j) Numerous other problems in mechanics and engineering

* Lemon, *From Galileo to Cosmic Rays*, p. 94.

The list above is not complete, but even the casual reader cannot fail to see that the extent of the application of the notion of the definite integral is bounded only by man's imagination and perseverance.

5. The indefinite integral. In the integral calculus there is also a second field of primary importance, the study of the **indefinite integral or anti-derivative.** For example, since $D(x^3/3 - 4x^2 + 2x + 3) = x^2 - 8x + 2$, we write

$$\int (x^2 - 8x + 2)dx = x^3/3 - 4x^2 + 2x + c$$

and say that the right member of the foregoing equation where c is any real number (cf. p. 139) is the indefinite integral or the anti-derivative of the function which appears in the left member under the integration sign. The indefinite integral does not have limits of integration; hence the terms in x cannot be replaced by numbers. For this reason the indefinite integral is not, like the definite integral, a number, but *it is a function of x.* The study of the relationship between the two functions which are thus related leads to interesting chapters in pure mathematics which are not lacking in important applications.

The operation of finding the indefinite integral is the inverse operation to that of finding the derivative.

CHAPTER 8

MATHEMATICAL INTERPRETATIONS OF
GEOMETRICAL AND PHYSICAL PHENOMENA*

MATHEMATICAL theories have been of great service in many experimental sciences in correlating the results of observations and in predicting new data afterward verified by observation. This has happened particularly in geometry, physics, and astronomy. But the relationship between a mathematical theory and the data which it is designed to relate is often misunderstood. When such a theory has been successful as a correlating agent, the conviction is likely to become established that the theory has a unique relationship to nature as interpreted for us by the observations. Furthermore, it is sometimes inferred that nature behaves in precisely the way which the mathematics indicates. As a matter of fact, nature never does behave in this way, and there are always more mathematical theories than one whose results depart from a given set of data by less than the errors of observation.

The purpose of this chapter is to explain in more detail the point of view which is indicated briefly in the preceding paragraph. A description will be given of the structures of pure and applied mathematical sciences. For this purpose the most accessible mathematical domain is geometry, and the first few paragraphs below are devoted to a discussion of various geometrical theories. But examples from astronomy and physics will also be briefly described in later sections.

1. Geometrical measurements. If our geometrical experiences were only those of very ancient peoples, our collection of observed geometric

* This chapter was written by G. A. Bliss, of the University of Chicago.

data would be a very limited one. Nowadays, however, we have many sources to draw from. We accumulate geometric data by measurements on the drawing-table, by local and geodetic surveys, by observing the motions of the planets, or even by the relatively very rough measurements of stellar distances which are now in use. In every case the measurements have a percentage of discrepancy which can be experimentally determined, and in every case the domain of observation is of finite extent.

On the drawing-table, for example, we designate as points the dots which we make with our pencil, and straight lines are the marks which we make by drawing the pencil along the edge of a ruler. It is not true experimentally, as we should perhaps like to have it, that every pair of dots is joined by one and only one straight line. If we were to sharpen our pencil sufficiently, and perhaps use a magnifying glass, we should see that a pair of dots can be joined by very many delicately drawn straight lines. It is likewise not true experimentally that the sum of the angles of a triangle is always 180°. If we measure our angles honestly, we find that the sum is usually not exactly 180°, but that the maximum variation of the sum from that amount is a small number, which depends upon the instruments used and the physical characteristics of the observer. Other observations which may be cited to illustrate the inaccuracy which attends all measurement are the measurements of stellar distances. The methods used are too technical to be described here. The points to be emphasized with regard to them are that even these enormous and almost incomprehensible distances are still finite, and that the percentage of inaccuracy in their determination is very great. That they can be estimated at all is a great tribute to the ingenuity of astronomers.

2. Fundamental postulates of geometry.* In view of the inaccuracy of geometrical observations it is clear that we can never hope to find a precise mathematical theory to correlate them which will be an exact fit. Until recently it has been customary to idealize points and lines. A point was something which had no dimensions; and a line had only one dimension, namely, length. We may still find such definitions in our textbooks. Unfortunately, our observational experience does not provide us with any

---

* Hilbert, *Foundations of Geometry* (Chicago: Open Court Pub. Co., 1902); Veblen and Young, *Projective Geometry*, Vol. I, Introduction and chapter i.

such geometrical entities. The dots and straight-line marks of the draw-ing-table certainly have dimensions; and it is, after all, their properties which our mathematical theory, whatever it may be, should correlate ap-proximately.

The procedure nowadays is quite different. We do not attempt to idealize points and lines. We rather try to construct an ideal geometrical theory by idealizing the fundamental properties which we ascribe to points and lines. The statements of these fundamental properties are called "pos-tulates"; and from them, by the processes of mathematical logic, are de-duced the theorems which constitute the exact science of geometry. Thus, in our ideal geometry one of the postulates is that two points can be joined by one and but one straight line. The dots and straight-line marks on the drawing-table do not satisfy this postulate, but the dots can be made so small that the eye alone cannot distinguish between the lines which join them. A theorem in our exact geometrical theory, based upon the postu-lates, should therefore correspond to a property of the dots and marks with a degree of approximation similar to that with which the postulate itself is applicable. Described somewhat roughly, the theorem should seem true to the unaided eye for dots and marks when the dots and marks are made sufficiently small.

The pure mathematician is, of course, primarily interested in exact abstract geometrical science, but he is guided in his selection of postulates by his observational experience. It is impossible here to give a complete list of the postulates for geometry. As formulated by the German mathe-matician, Hilbert, they are twenty in number and are of five types, which are called the postulates of "connection," "order," "congruence," "paral-lelism," and "continuity." Examples of each of these will be given in the following paragraphs.

The postulate mentioned above, stating that through two points there passes one and but one line, is a postulate of connection. There are six others of this type. If three points lie on the same line, then one and only one of them lies between the other two. This is a postulate concern-ing order. It seems self-evident unless we recognize, for example, that of three lines through a point each one may be regarded as lying between the other two. By this example we see that there are other types of order be-sides that described in the postulate concerning the order of the points on a line, and that therefore some agreement about the order of such points is necessary if our geometry is to have a sound basis. There are, in all, five postulates concerning order. If two triangles have two sides and the included angle of the one equal to two sides and the included angle of the other, then the other two pairs of homologous angles of the triangle are congruent. This postulate belongs to the basis of that part of geometry which has to do with congruent triangles. It is a sample of the postulates of congruence, which are six in number.

Now we come to the famous assumption of Euclid concerning parallel lines. If a line l and a point P are given, then there is one and but one line through P which has no point in common with l. This is not by any means a self-evident property of the straight lines of our experience, though geometers for many centuries thought that it was so or that it could be proved to be a consequence of other simple postulates. No one was able to make such a proof; and when another geometrical theory was found with this postulate changed, but all the others just the same, it became evident that no proof of the dependence of Euclid's postulate could ever be made. The possibility of changing the postulate to another is a consequence of the facts noted above, that all of our geometrical experiences are in a finite portion of space and that our geometrical measurements agree only to within a certain percentage of discrepancy. That two postulational bases differing in this way are possible will perhaps be clearer after we have considered in the next section an example of a geometry in which Euclid's postulate is not true, but which nevertheless correlates the facts of our geometrical experience with as high a degree of accuracy as does Euclid's geometry itself.

The final postulate which we shall consider, the so-called "postulate of continuity," is usually ascribed to the famous old Greek scientist, Archimedes. If A, A_1, and B are three points in that order on a line, then there is always a sequence of points A, A_1, A_2, ... , A_n such that the segments between adjacent points are all congruent, and, furthermore, such that B lies between A and A_n. This is equivalent to saying that, by starting at A and laying off successively equal segments, we can always ultimately pass the point B.

It will be noted that all of the postulates which have been stated above are in accord with our geometrical instincts. They and the others, which for want of space could not be mentioned, are statements of simple properties of points and lines which we intuitively willingly adopt as proper bases for a geometrical theory, and which agree to a suitable degree of approximation with geometrical data on the drawing-table or in any other finite region where such data are obtainable. It is clear that none of us can follow two lines out to more than a very limited distance to see if they ever meet, and none of us can check the postulate of Archimedes for points B which are very far away. We select these postulates because we like them and think that they will help to give us a useful theory.

3. **A simple non-Euclidean geometry.** Examples of sets of geometrical data which can be correlated by two different geometrical theories are very common. The surveyor, for example, uses the formulas of plane geometry when he measures the area of a city lot or of a farm. Theoretically, he should, of course, use spherical geometry, since his measurements are made on the spherical surface of the earth. It would be foolish of him to do so, however, since the formulas of plane geometry are much easier to work with than those of spherical geometry, and since for a small area the surface of the earth is so nearly a plane that no ordinary surveying instrument could ever distinguish between the two. Evidently in this case either of the two theories would give results in agreement with observed data to a high degree of precision. The choice between the two for practical work is made for reasons of simplicity and convenience.

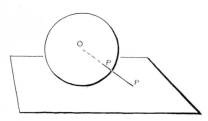

Just as the surveyor uses plane, instead of spherical, formulas for measurements on a sphere, so one may interpret plane geometrical phenomena by a spherical theory. To see this, let us consider a very large sphere resting on a plane table-top. We may associate with each point P on the plane the point on the sphere which is the intersection of the straight line joining P to the center of the sphere. The points of a segment of a straight line in the plane then correspond to those of a segment of a great circle on the sphere. If we define the length of a line segment as the length of the corresponding great circle segment on the sphere, and make a similar definition for the measurement of angles, a new geometrical theory for the plane can be constructed.

It should be noted, first of all, that when the sphere is sufficiently large the new measures for segments and angles on the table agree with those of ordinary Euclidean geometry so closely that no measuring instrument, however delicate, could ever distinguish between them. Every straight line has a finite length, in the new geometry, equal to the length of half of a great circle on the sphere. The sum of the angles of a triangle on the plane is greater than 180°, since the sum of the angles of a triangle on the sphere has this property. Finally, we see that through a point P outside of a line l there passes no line parallel to l. Every pair of lines in the plane has a common point at a finite distance, since every pair of great circles on the sphere has a point of intersection. Thus Euclid's postulate is not true in the new geometry. These discrepancies with Euclid's theory need not disturb us at all, however, as far as our interpretations of geometrical data on the table-top are concerned. In this limited domain the two theories agree so closely that either one offers an acceptable explanation. We should be foolish to select the spherical theory for practical purposes, however, since the formulas of spherical geometry are much more complicated than those of Euclidean geometry in the plane.

In concluding our consideration of this example, it should be stated that there are many other mathematical theories for the interpretation of geometrical phenomena in the plane. The theory which has been suggested above was discovered by Riemann and is sometimes called "Riemannian non-Euclidean geometry." There are also geometries in which through each point P not on a line l there pass an infinity of lines not meeting l. These lines through P form a sheaf so thin that it is not distinguishable experimentally from a single line.

4. The structure of a mathematical science. A pure mathematical science consists of postulates, definitions, and theorems. Thus for geometry we agree, first of all, that the names of elements to be studied shall be points and lines, and we postulate a set of simple properties for these elements from which all other properties are to be deduced. We define in terms of points and lines what we mean by an angle, a triangle, a polygon, or a circle; and, starting from the postulates, we prove by processes of mathematical logic the theorems concerning the things so defined which constitute the important results of geometrical science.

The science of arithmetic has a similar structure. The postulates for positive integers are four in number.* For two such integers we can define what we mean by the sum, product, difference, and quotient; and we can prove for these the well-known laws of computation, such as the theorem that the product of a number of integers has the same value irrespective of the order in which the integers are taken. Furthermore, starting from the positive integers and their properties, we can define and analyze the properties of the complete system of positive and negative real numbers. Thus we see again that arithmetic is a science consisting of postulates, definitions, and theorems.

An applied mathematical science has a somewhat more complicated structure. The physicist, astronomer, or geometer frequently finds himself in possession of a set of data, obtained by observation, which he would like to correlate by means of a mathematical theory of the kind described in the two preceding paragraphs. For this purpose he must, first of all, select a set of postulates, as simple as possible, which are in agreement with the observed data as nearly as the observations are in agreement with themselves. When the logical consequences of the postulates have been worked out, he must devise new experiments, if necessary, to check again with observation his theoretical results. Thus the structure of an applied mathematical science can be suggested by the accompanying table.

	Observed data	
Postulates	Postulates	. . . .
Definitions	Definitions	. . . .
Theorems	Theorems	. . . .
	Check with observed data	

The form of the table indicates that for the correlation of observed data it is to be expected that more than one mathematical theory may be effective, as we have seen above in the case of geometry. The selection of one among the theories possible is based on convenience, or on accuracy of fit with the data, or both. There is danger always, when a theory has been found to be convenient and effective over a long period of time, that people may begin to think that Nature herself behaves precisely in the way which is indicated by the theory. This is never the case, and the

* See, for example, Landau, *Grundlagen der Analysis*, chap. i, and chap. 2, sec. 10, of this book.

belief that it is so may close our minds to other possible theories and be a serious impediment to progress in the development of our interpretations of the world around us.

Just as the same set of data may be related by more than one mathematical theory, so it is possible that the same theory may be effective in connection with more than one set of data. If we define a point to be a pair (x, y) of real numbers, and a straight line to be the totality of pairs (x, y) which satisfy an equation of the form $ax+by+c=0$, we may prove that these points and lines satisfy precisely the postulates of Euclidean plane geometry. Thus the science of geometry is applicable not only approximately to the dots and straight-line marks of the drawing-table but also with exactitude to the number-pairs and linear equations of the Cartesian coordinate system. By the mechanism of such a coordinate system we thus bring to bear on geometry the powerful and familiar processes of arithmetic. The theory of geometry from this point of view is called "analytic geometry."

In concluding this section it should be re-emphasized that the purposes of an applied mathematical science are twofold: first to correlate and systematize data which may otherwise appear heterogeneous and unrelated in character, and second to predict by logical processes new results which might be difficult or impossible to discover by experimental methods alone. Many examples of the effectiveness of mathematical theories in both of these respects could be given if space permitted.

The astronomer

5. Mathematical theories in astronomy. The Ptolemaic and Copernican theories of the solar system are excellent examples of theories widely different in character but which, with suitable modifications of the former, describe with equal accuracy the motions of the planets. In the Ptolemaic theory the earth is regarded as the center of the solar system. The stars and the sun move on circles with the earth very near the centers, and in the modification suggested by Tycho Brahe the planets move on circles whose centers are at the sun and move with the sun. The curves thus described by the planets, as seen from the earth, are called "epicycloids." This is approximately the picture which we see when we stand out on the lawn and observe the heavens, and it has much to recommend it. Numerically, it is not sufficiently accurate for astronomical purposes, but it could be made so by replacing the circles by ellipses and superposing a suitable perturbation theory. In the familiar and more popular Copernican theory, the sun is the central body of the solar system and the stars are fixed. The earth and the other planets move about the sun on ellipses each of which has the sun as a focus. The mathematical justification of the motions of the planets in either theory is based upon the famous Law of Gravitation of Newton.

There is really no advantage for either of these theories as compared with the other, as far as their adaptability to explain numerically the facts of the solar system is concerned. The Copernican theory is, however, much the simpler geometrically and mathematically. For this reason it has been adopted and developed until astronomers can predict coming celestial events with most surprising accuracy; and it has resulted in the discovery of the two outmost planets, Neptune and Pluto.

But even the Copernican theory based upon Newtonian mechanics has failed to fit all of the observed data satisfactorily. The perihelion of a planet is the point nearest to the sun on its elliptical orbit. According to Newtonian mechanics, the perihelion of the inmost planet, Mercury, should move about the sun each year a distance which differs from the observed motion by a perceptible amount. Many explanations for this discrepancy have been offered, but none of them was well received by astronomers until Einstein suggested a slight modification of Newtonian mechanics itself, in accord with his so-called general "theory of relativity." The new theory agrees with observed data, including the motion of the perihelion of Mercury, with discrepancies which are less than the errors of observation; but it is much less convenient for computation than the Newtonian theory. For most purposes we can still retain Newtonian mechanics, since the two theories disagree by less than the errors of observation in all except a very few instances.

The theory of general relativity as applied to the solar system is already threatened, even before its usefulness has been completely established. Recently, when Einstein and de Sitter were sojourning in the United States, the newspapers reported them as discussing still newer theories from which it might be concluded that the universe is finite. This conclusion should never be made. All that we could be justified in saying is that the data which we have concerning the distances and motions of the stars are in closer accord with a theory which is finite than with others which have not this property. The finiteness which can be demonstrated is a property of the theory and not of the universe. By a finite theory we mean one, such as the Riemannian geometry described in a preceding section, in which the distances of all points from any given fixed point are finite. The geometrical theory of Euclid has not this property.

6. Mathematical theories in physics. The physicist makes use of mathematics primarily as a correlator of heterogeneous data. One of the best examples of the possibility of using two slightly different theories for the correlation of the same physical phenomena lies in the relationship between Newtonian mechanics and the mechanics of the special theory of relativity. Every event in physical experience occurs at a particular time and place. If an observer A has a rectangular system of coordinates in space and a mechanism for measuring time, he can locate each event by giving its time, t, and its three space coordinates, x, y, z. Thus the location of an event requires the specification of four num-

The physicist

bers t, x, y, z. This is all that the mathematical physicist means when he says that the world of events is a four-dimensional world.

If a second observer A' is moving with constant velocity v in the direction of the positive x-axis of the system of coordinates of A, and if A' has a clock and a system of space coordinates parallel to those of A and moving with A', then each event will have four coordinates—t', x', y', z'—for A', as well as the four coordinates t, x, y, z of A. Newtonian mechanics tells us that these two sets of coordinates are related by equations of the form

$$t'=t, \quad x'=x-vt, \quad y'=y, \quad z'=z . \tag{1}$$

The special theory of relativity asserts, on the other hand, that these relations should be replaced by the equations

$$t' = \beta(t - vx/c^2), \quad x' = \beta(x - vt), \quad y' = y, \quad z' = z, \tag{2}$$

in which c is the velocity of light and β is merely a convenient symbol for the more complicated expression $\beta = 1/(1 - v^2/c^2)^{1/2}$. It is unnecessary here to explain in detail the derivation of either of these sets of equations. For both theories they enable us to calculate the coordinates t', x', y', z' of an event when the coordinates t, x, y, z are given, or vice versa. Such relations are, of course, necessary if the world of events as observed by one of A and A' is to have any meaning to the other. Since the velocity of light in kilometers per second is the very large number $c = 300,000$, it is evident that for velocities v not exceeding a few kilometers per second the ratio v/c is exceedingly small and the value of β is very near to unity, so that the formulas (2) are almost identical with formulas (1). Thus, for all moving bodies which we ordinarily consider on the surface of the earth, or for the motions of the planets, the two sets of equations give sets of values t', x', y', z' which are experimentally indistinguishable. The velocities of electrons in a current passing through a vacuum tube may, however, be a large fraction of c. For such cases the formulas (2) have been found to give results which agree with observations much better than those given by equations (1). Here, then, are two theories whose

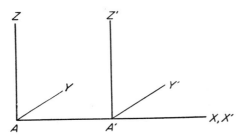

results differ by less than the errors of observation for everyday velocities. But one of them has a much better fit with observed data than the other when the range of velocities is enlarged.

The equations (2) are fundamental in the deduction of many of the results of the special relativity theory. From them we can prove as mathematical theorems the often quoted assertions that, according to the special theory of relativity, a clock runs slower when it is moving than when it is stationary, that a yardstick is shortened when moving in the direction of its length, or that there exist events occurring in one time order for A which appear to A' to take place in the opposite order. We need not worry about these matters from the practical standpoint, for the retardation of the clock and the shortening of the yardstick at any velocities which we can experimentally impose upon them are too small to be measured by any apparatus which we now possess, and events whose orders are inverted must be so near together as to be practically indistinguishable.

As a final example of applied mathematical theories in physics, one should mention the quantum theory. It is perhaps the most recently developed of all mathematical-physical theories, and is still undergoing modification and improvement. When an electric current consisting of electrons is passed through rarefied hydrogen gas in a vacuum tube, the atoms of the gas are excited and give off radiation which has a very definite and well-known line spectrum. One of the fundamental problems of the quantum theory is the determination of the character of the atoms of hydrogen and the mechanism by means of which they can give off the observed radiation. In the Bohr theory the atom is a tiny solar system consisting of a nucleus and an electron moving about each other in accord with a modified Newtonian theory of mechanics. By Newtonian mechanics the positions and velocities of the particles constituting the atom are determined uniquely at all times t when their positions and velocities at one time are known. This fact is a mathematical expression of the so-called "principle of cause and effect." A second theory, matrix mechanics, provides for each time t only percentages of probability that the particles will be in various positions or have various velocities. According to this theory, we would conclude that among the myriad of atoms of hydrogen in the tube a certain percentage have their particles in one position at a given time t; a second percentage have their particles in another; and so on. In some cases one of the percentages may be 100, or very nearly 100, and then we know with great precision what to expect. But in the quantum theory it is a theorem that in no case can a probability for positions and a probability for velocities be simultaneously 100. Thus we can never expect to have accurate information about positions and velocities at the same time. This, very roughly, is a description of the now famous "principle of uncertainty" of matrix mechanics, as contrasted to the principle of cause and effect of the older Newtonian theory. The principle of uncertainty has caused much discussion among philosophers and physicists, since it seems to affect fundamentally our conception of the universe of phenomena in which we find ourselves immersed. If we accept the point of view of the preceding paragraphs, however, we must agree that the universe itself, sparsely interpreted for us by disconnected data, is not affected by either of these theories. Neither the principle of cause and effect nor the principle of uncertainty can be precisely characteristic of the behavior of nature. They are merely most interesting theorems in two different theories by means of which we endeavor to correlate and interpret observed data. The ultimate choice between the two theories must be determined by convenience or by their relative accuracies of fit with observation, and not because of any supposedly precise correspondence with nature on the part of either one of them.

CHAPTER 9

MATHEMATICS AND LIFE

ON THE second floor of the Hall of Science at the Century of Progress Exposition, held at Chicago in the summers of 1933 and 1934, reaching up into the great tower of the building was a smaller tower designed to symbolize the interrelations and the interdependence of the physical sciences. The huge base on which the remaining sciences were supported and uplifted was assigned to mathematics. Astronomy, physics, chemistry, the medical sciences, geology, geography, engineering, architecture, the industrial arts—all had their roots in the science by whose methods and attainments they have learned and continue to learn to express themselves. It would have been equally appropriate if a similar tower had been placed in the Hall of the Social Sciences, for here, too, mathematical theories and mathematical methods are of prime importance in the development of these fields of knowledge. To quote from Adolphe Quételet (1796–1874), the great Belgian astronomer, mathematician, anthropometrist, economist, and statistician:*

The more advanced the sciences have become, the more they have tended to enter the domain of mathematics, which is a sort of center towards which they converge. We can judge of the perfection to which a science has come by the facility, more or less great, by which it can be approached by calculation.

In this chapter will be discussed very briefly a few of the uncounted number of the contributions of mathematics to the safety, comfort, health,

---

* *National Council of Teachers of Mathematics, Sixth Yearbook* (Bureau of Publications, Teachers College, Columbia University, 1931), p. 112. Hereafter this work will be referred to as the *Sixth Yearbook*.

convenience, progress, and pleasures of man. If you are interested to read further, the appended Bibliography will prove useful both for the information which it represents and for further references which it will provide.

1. Mathematics reveals the heavens. Primitive man measured time by the alternation of light and darkness caused by the rotation of the earth on its axis and by the phases of the moon. Later, the recurrence of the seasons suggested a longer time unit, the year. Many were the attempts to make a calendar or "mode of adjusting the natural divisions of time with respect to each other for the purposes of civil life," but no calendar constructed before 1582 was accurate. The consequence was that after the lapse of sufficient time the accumulated error amounted to days or even weeks.

The reason for this difficulty is that there is no unit of measure which can be applied simultaneously to the period of the earth's rotation on its axis, the period of the moon's revolution about the earth, and the period of the earth's revolution about the sun. The three time-intervals are mutually *incommensurable*.

The Babylonian division of the year has been described on page 18. Other early calendars had a year consisting of twelve lunar months, giving a total of 354 days. A little computation

Time and the calendar

will show you that, if you were using such a calendar, it would not be many years before Christmas would be coming in August instead of December. In 46 B.C. Julius Caesar, with the help of the Alexandrian astronomer Sosigines, undertook a thorough reform of the calendar. His new calendar, called the *Julian calendar*, was adopted by most of the civilized nations; but, since the Julian year was 11 minutes and a few seconds too short, at the time the *Gregorian calendar* was devised in 1582 it was necessary to annul 10 days. This was accomplished by a papal bull which decreed that the day following the 4th of October in that year should be the 15th of October.

Furthermore, the new calendar provides that years which are multiples of 100 shall *not* be leap years unless they are also multiples of 400.

The Gregorian calendar is in use at the present time in almost all of the countries of the earth, and it is sufficiently accurate to be satisfactory. The error is 3 days in about 10,000 years. However, there are many persons who advocate the adoption of a new calendar which shall not have the disadvantages of unequal months and unequal quarters. One which has been suggested divides the years into thirteen months of 28 days each. The one remaining day in a common year and the two remaining days in a leap year are to be world-holidays, called "year days," and are not to be considered as belonging to any one of the months. A second suggested calendar proposes to have twelve months with the number of days apportioned so as to make *equal quarters;* in each quarter will be three months having 31, 30, and 30 days, respectively. At the meeting of the Mathematical Association of America at St. Louis on Monday, December 30, 1935, the adoption of the equal-quarters calendar was recommended. A committee of the League of Nations is studying the implications of these suggested changes; we shall await with interest its report.

The science of astronomy, with its remarkably high accuracy relative to measurement of distances and of periodic motion, has made possible the construction of accurate calendars. This science of astronomy has evolved by slow and painful stages from astrology—a queer mixture of facts, fancies, and superstitions which purported to associate the temperament and destiny of persons with the heavenly configurations at the time of birth. The foundations of these superstitions were sapped by Copernicus, Galileo, Tycho Brahe, and Kepler; while with Newton, astronomy emerged from mystery and astrology passed into the hands of quacks.

Astronomy

Without clocks, calendars, astronomical clocks, and chronometers, used in determining longitude at sea, the hazards of travel by train or by boat would be so great that few would venture to travel far.

A second interesting mathematical chapter in the history of astronomy is that which began with the belief that the earth is the center of the universe, about which the heavens and the sun in the heavens turn, and ended with the Law of Gravitation of Newton. It follows from this law that the sun and the earth turn around the center of gravity of the system, a point which lies in the interior of the sun on a line joining their centers. Moreover, we can compute with precision the period of the revolution about the sun of each of its satellites, predicting with accuracy not only such phenomena as eclipses but also the return of comets.

In the interval outlined above we have the superstitions of the astrologers concerning the influence of the heavenly bodies on the inhabitants of the earth; the philosophy of the philosophers who made their own assumptions and argued to their logical conclusions; the recorded observations from Hipparchus to Tycho Brahe; the attempt at interpretation of Ptolemy; the stupendous computations of Kepler, in which he endeavored to reconcile the Ptolemaic theory with the observations of his master, Tycho Brahe; and finally, the mathematical solution of the problem, viz.,

The planets move about the sun in ellipses with the sun at one of the foci.

2. Mathematics reveals the earth. The determination of the shape, size, mass, density, and motions of the earth are problems of the mathematical astronomer. The geographer studies the surface of the earth and

Geography

supplies us with information which is of interest to us as individuals, of practical value to the business man who wishes to trade with those of other parts, of importance to the navigator who guides his ship from port to port, and of great value to the governments of the world in the regulation of trade and of the tariff.

The geographer's chief tool for the dissemination of his knowledge is his map. It is not a simple matter to project a portion of the earth's surface on a plane without annoying and dangerous distortion. The construction and the understanding of the Mercator maps and the Goode maps, which are in general use, require a knowledge of higher mathematics.

Astronomers, philosophers, religious leaders, and mathematical astronomers have, from time to time, advanced theories concerning the origin of the solar system and the origin of the earth; but it remained for a geologist, Thomas Chrowder Chamberlin, to conceive the theory of the *Planetesimal hypothesis* of the origin of the solar system. This hypothesis is steadily growing in favor with modern scientists. Professor Chamberlin, a geologist and not a mathematician, before he presented his theory to the world, called to his aid the mathematical astronomer, Forest Ray Moulton, who, basing his computations on the Law of Gravitation, was able to show that the Planetesimal hypothesis is a mathematically possible explanation of the origins of the satellites of the sun and of their satellites, as well as of the origins of their motions. He also showed that the origins of these motions could not be explained by the earlier theory due to Laplace, the *Nebular hypothesis.*

3. Mathematics underlies the physical sciences. Let us attempt to imagine what would happen if all mathematical formulas were suddenly to disappear from our scientific literature and from the minds of our physicists, chemists, engineers, and astronomers. Not only would we face the hazards of transportation mentioned in a previous paragraph; but the telephone, telegraph, radio, and wireless would cease to function, factories would close, building would come to a standstill, business communication would come to a halt, pestilence and famine would be rampant.

The transmission of more than one telegraph message over a single pair of wires is made possible by means of wave-filters designed upon a purely mathematical theory. A "coaxial" cable which will carry 240 telephone talks on a high-grade television circuit was announced by the Bell system in 1935. When the laying of a submarine cable across the Atlantic was first contemplated, the advice of a scientist, Lord Kelvin, was sought. He advised that the cable be worked at lower potentials than those which were proposed by the first engineer of the project. The engineer did not heed his advice, and the cable collapsed.

The life of Charles Proteus Steinmetz (1865–1923) reads like a fairy tale. He was a man of the highest genius with a well-trained mind and an unlimited capacity for work. His work in his experimental laboratory and his scientific interpretation of his results brought him recognition as an important instrument in the growth and expansion of the General Electric Company, for which he was consulting engineer.

The formula for an electric flatiron which automatically breaks the current when a given temperature is reached, and automatically re-estab-

Physics

lishes the connection when a given lower temperature is attained, was found by a mathematician after a short computation; it had been sought in an experimental laboratory for months.

The theory and science of geometrical and physical optics has as its basis a geometrical theory of form. Eye lenses, microscopes, telescopes, the mutual relations of light and electricity, the optical phenomena of the atmosphere—these are some, but not all, of the ramifications of this subject.

Other physical theories which are highly mathematical are: thermodynamics, the theory of the spinning electron in its relation to the X-ray, the problem of n bodies (originally an astronomical problem) in its relation to the study of the atom and its spectra, the quantum theory, crystal structure, the theory of relativity, the investigation of cosmic rays, and the subjects of keen interest to the general public, viz., television and talking motion pictures.

Under the same heading, "mathematical physics," stand the two subjects of interior ballistics and the applications of mathematics to aeronautics. During the critical years from 1914 to 1918 a staff of mathematicians at the Aberdeen Proving Ground studied the former in all of its phases. An exposition of the new and remarkable findings of himself and others was published by F. R. Moulton (see Bibliography).

In regard to aeronautics, the past few years have witnessed the publication of numerous memoirs, a few of which are listed at the end of the chapter. Such subjects as potential air flow about the wings of an airplane; the dangerous type of wing oscillation general- ly (but inappropriately) de- scribed by the gentle word "flutter"; vibrations of pro- peller, wings, or engine; sound and noise in aircraft; the cool- ing of aircraft engines—all of these are now being studied by trained mathematicians.

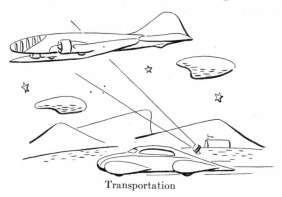

Transportation

One of the comparatively recent discoveries is the photoelectric cell, called the *electric eye*. It is used in broadcasting television, in photometry, in opening and closing doors, and in sound reproductions. Persons sepa- rated by many miles are enabled to carry on a conversation, using as a transmission medium a beam of light directed toward a photoelectric cell. One of the most impor- tant uses of the electric eye will undoubted- ly be in the field of aviation.

The electric eye

The electronic cell, called the *third eye*, was first announced to the public by its inventor, Dr. Vladimir K. Zworykin, of the Radio Corporation of America, at the meeting of the American Association for the Advancement of Science at St. Louis on January 2, 1936. It is an electron tube which literally sees the invisible and includes the infra-red and the ultra-violet for the first time in man's range of vision, thus almost quadrupling the range of the human eye.* Instead of light, this eye uses electrons, focusing them on a fluo- rescent screen which plays the rôle of the eye's retina. It can be used both for telescopic and for microscopic work.

* Heretofore the infra-red and ultra-violet portions of the spectrum have been accessible only through the use of photographic instruments.

Another important demonstration at the St. Louis meeting was that of the new giant nine-lens photographic machine which has just been completed by Sherman M. Fairchild for the United States Geodetic Survey. The camera uses one large film which weighs 25 lb. and can take 100 exposures for all lenses. It can photograph 600 sq. mi. of the earth's surface at one simultaneous exposure at an altitude of 30,000 ft.

We probably have not thought that mathematics is of much importance in agriculture; but, according to Harry Burgess Roe,*

The modern farmer, if he is to be successful, must be a business man in the fullest sense. He must have in his mental equipment a larger and broader knowledge of scientific, economic, and financial principles than that required in almost any other line of business in the world to-day in order that he may plan, direct, and carry out the operation of his farm intelligently and with profit. He must be able to plan the size and arrangement of buildings on the farmstead, to subdivide his farm into fields of the proper shape, size, and arrangement for economical and balanced operation, to plan suitable rotations, to inaugurate and carry out systems of fertilization and pest control, to build a farm calendar, and to schedule the amount and distribution of all man and horse labor and mechanical power. He must know something of the relative efficiency of methods and equipment as well as of the principles of depreciation and replacement of both machinery and livestock. He must balance his crop production to meet the needs of his livestock, and he must plan his feeding rations and select and breed new strains in both crops and livestock to insure the best results in production. He must be able to estimate the amount of paint required for a building, or the best shape or size for a given field to be fenced with a known amount of fencing. He must know the capacities of men and machinery, of bins and buildings. He must have a knowledge of financing that includes investments, income, loans, capitalization, and amortization. Above all, he must know markets, be able to build comparative tables and charts of yields, costs of production, and prices through a series of years, and from these to forecast, with reasonable assurance, the prospects for the current and the coming year for the various crops, as a guide to his general plan of farming for that year.

This is a large contract and it is plainly to be seen that it involves a practical knowledge of mathematics far beyond the scope of the traditional third R of our grandfather's day. It includes mensuration, proportion, rates and the compound interest idea in annuities and amortization, graphs and their interpretation, frequency distribution, and the application of mathematics to the elementary principles and practice of surveying.

* *Sixth Yearbook*, pp. 86 ff.

4. Mathematics underlies the biological sciences. Not until a few decades ago did biologists extend the scope of their studies to include comparison and interpretation as well as description and classification. The latter, description and classification, gave to us great museums filled with carefully preserved and minutely described specimens of plants and animals, and numerous books of flora and fauna and masterly treatises on anatomy and embryology. The more recent comparative and interpretative studies have led to the investigation of physical and chemical processes which occur in the living organisms, notably in the theory of the development and division of the cell. Physics and chemistry are quantitive; and to a high degree, mathematical sciences. Conse-

Chemistry

quently, biologists have been forced more and more to take over the mathematical methods of expression and analysis characteristic of these sciences. The biometric methods, i.e., the use of mathematical formulas suitable for the analysis of the complex and highly variable data of biological observation and measurement, are now being applied by some of the leading scholars in biological, sociological, and psychological experimental investigations.

In a paper entitled "Mathematics in Biology,"* by the late Professor J. Arthur Harris of the University of Minnesota, we read:

In the future, mathematics will have an increasing influence in determining the direction of research. This is due not solely to the fact that the biometric formulas facilitate the solution of many problems, but also to the fact that after a certain stage in science is reached, calculation is to some degree capable of anticipating the results of experimentation. The value of the mathematician's prediction is well known to the physicist, the chemist, and the astronomer. As yet little progress in this direction has been made in biology, but I am glad to go on record as predicting that before many years have passed experimentation will be to a considerable extent guided by preliminary calculation.

* *Sixth Yearbook*, p. 18. The article is adapted from one which appeared in the *Scientific Monthly* for August, 1928.

My second point has to deal with a very different matter. Elegance of form has always made a very powerful appeal to the mathematician. As the biologist is forced by the inevitable progress of his science to occupy himself more and more with mathematical literature, its logic, terseness, and elegance of expression must have an influence on his own standards of presentation.

It is not possible to follow the courses in the professional schools of medicine, pharmacy, dentistry, and nursing without a certain amount of elementary mathematical training, while many phases of research in these fields require the use of the methods of the calculus and, frequently, of higher mathematics. Professor Edward Spease,* of the School of Pharmacy, Western Reserve University, says:

> The best advice that a teacher can give to a boy or girl planning to enter any one of these professions is to take all the mathematics his high school offers. I do not say definitely that a student who has not had all the mathematics available in a high school will fail in one of these professions. I do say that I have never known one who has had such work to fail and I do know that the student who is good in mathematics and who has taken much of it finds his professional work far easier.

Professor Louis C. Thurstone, of the University of Chicago, is using the theory of matrices in the analysis of multiple factors. He has developed methods for isolating fundamental and elementary factors in psychological, social, and biological phenomena. The general nature of the factor problem can be stated rather briefly. Let each one of a group of N individuals be described with regard to n attributes or composite traits. Further, let it be the hypothesis of an investigator that these n traits are made up of a relatively small number, $r < n$, of elementary factors. His object is to discover these elementary factors.

If each one of the N individuals is rated with regard to each one of n traits, these ratings can be tabulated in an $N \times n$ table or matrix. If the elementary factors can be isolated and if each one of the N individuals is rated with regard to each one of the r elementary factors, these more fundamental ratings would fill an $N \times r$ table, where $r < n$. Further, if each one of the n traits can be comprehended in terms of r elementary factors, these data would fill an $n \times r$ table. The scientific problem is to find the simplest form of this $n \times r$ table.

* *Sixth Yearbook*, p. 104.

As a first approximation it is assumed that each of the n traits can be comprehended as a linear function of the r elementary factors. Each trait is then regarded as a weighted sum of the elementary factors. The complete table would contain the nr weights. But this is not necessarily the simplest way to comprehend the n traits. It may be possible so to choose the elementary factors that a very large proportion of the weight-entries vanish. If that is the case, then perhaps each one of the n traits can be comprehended in terms of less than the full set of r factors. If a trait is represented by one of the rows in the $n \times r$ table, perhaps all but one, or two, or three, of the r weight-entries vanish. When this type of overdetermined simplicity is discovered in a set of experimental data, it can be assumed that the simplicity has been not produced by chance, but that the factors refer to meaningful elementary factors. The $n \times r$ table of weights then shows the simplest possible linear interpretation of the n traits in the N individuals. When this overdetermined simplicity is found, it is called a *simple structure* or *simple configuration*. The factors so found constitute fundamental concepts for the science that is partially represented in the traits.

5. Mathematics underlies the social sciences. In the studies that are being made in the social sciences, the usefulness of mathematical methods and mathematical theories is becoming increasingly apparent. Mortality tables, the basis used by actuaries for calculating life insurance premiums, are constructed by "smoothing" statistical data, i.e., by constructing formulas and curves which approximate more or less closely the data at hand. Once constructed, these formulas and curves are treated as continuous representations of the relationship between the quantities considered, and provide, as one example, the expectancy of life of an individual of any given age. Professor Irving Fisher,* of Yale University, says:

Recently, with the development of statistics of industry, the art of curve fitting, by mathematical methods, has grown very rapidly, and examples of it will be found in many current issues of statistical journals. . . . . One important phase of curve fitting which links it closely with the study of economic theory is the statistical evaluation of supply and demand curves. . . . . Professor Henry

* *Bulletin of the American Mathematical Society*, April, 1930.

Schultz of the University of Chicago was apparently the first to work out the statistical determination of the effect of the tariff on the price of an important commodity—sugar.

In his more recent work, Professor Schultz studies, as a mathematical problem, the relations of demand, price, and income. He obtains a differential equation which expresses the rate of change of the individual's demand (or supply) with respect to its price, as a function of all the prices, all the initial quantities (income), and all the marginal utility functions. His computed results are in close agreement with known statistical data. This is a fundamental step in the development of an empirical science of economics which will be a better approximation to the facts of our economic life than theories heretofore advanced.

The theories of correlation and of probability are of fundamental importance in the interpretation and application of the results of studies of this nature. The fields of application include not only economics but all other branches of the social sciences—sociology, anthropology, and education—as well as psychology, biology, hygiene, and eugenics in the biological sciences.

While it is true that much of the work of the statistician has been accomplished with little mathematical technique beyond algebra, the pure economists are beginning to make considerable use of the differential and integral calculus and of the vector analysis developed by J. Willard Gibbs (1839–1903). I quote now from the late Professor Marshall* of Cambridge University:

A great change in the manner of thought has been brought about during the present generation by the general adoption of semi-mathematical language for expressing the relation between small increments of a commodity on the one hand, and on the other hand small increments in the aggregate price that will be paid for it: and by formally describing these small increments of price as measuring corresponding small increments of pleasure. . . . .

A training in mathematics is helpful by giving command over a marvellously terse and exact language for expressing clearly some general relations and some short processes of economic reasoning; which can indeed be expressed in ordinary language, but not with equal sharpness of outline. And, what is of far greater importance, experience in handling physical problems by mathematical methods gives a grasp, that cannot be obtained equally well in any other way, of the

* *Sixth Yearbook*, p. 9.

mutual interaction of economic changes. The direct application of mathematical reasoning to the discovery of economic truths has recently rendered great services in the hands of master mathematicians to the studies of statistical averages and probabilities and in measuring the degree of consilience between correlated statistical tables.

With this point of view, the economist can deal, not only with high price and low price, but with *rate of price change*, which, Professor Marshall shows, has important theoretical and practical effects on the rate of interest and on the volume of business.

6. Mathematics underlies machine design and construction. It supplies the formulas for all forms of engines and mechanical apparatus, whether operated by hand, by steam, by oil, gas, or electricity.

When large numbers of a given small part of a machine are turned out, not all are perfect. By a mathematical theory it is easily determined how much deviation from the model can be permitted without impairing the efficiency of the machine, and an application of the (mathematical) theory of *sampling* shows whether a given lot of these parts measures up to the required standard. In the Ford building at the Century of Progress Exposition was a machine which checked automatically both for length and diameter a certain type of small part used in the making of Ford cars. This machine is a mechanical substitute for the theory of sampling, which in its turn has been used to replace the former expensive method of checking each piece by hand.

Modern transportation is rendered less hazardous by the use of the radio and of wireless, neither of which could have been developed without a knowledge of mathematics.

7. Mathematics underlies all study of form. The ramifications here are noteworthy, viz., form as studied by the structural engineer who builds bridges, dams, etc.; form as it interests the architect; and form as an expression of symmetry and beauty.

There is at Quebec a bridge with a very long span. It was built in three parts, one part built up from each side, and then the central part, which had been constructed separately, was to be put in place. Twice the attempt to do this ended in disaster. Such an event must always end in disaster unless mathematical calculations have been made with great care. The dimensions must be exactly right, the machinery used in lift-

ing and in moving parts must be adequate to support the loads, and there must be perfect control of motion.

Modern building processes are vastly differ-ent from those of only a few decades ago. When the cabin in which Lincoln was born was built, there was a minimum of structural engineering. The rafters of the roof had to be mitered, the door and the windows fitted into the openings left for them. No frame and no buttresses were needed, because the logs were heavy enough to bear the thrust of the roof, even though they were

Architecture

merely chinked together with Kentucky clay. The architect, the late Mr. Bertram Goodhue, who planned the chapel of the University of Chicago had a real mathematical problem to solve. He succeeded in so choosing his proportions and decorative units that he gave us a building which not only is structurally sound but is a joy to behold.

Many of the buildings at the Century of Progress Exposition were constructed in parts in factories. When the parts were assembled at the site where the building was to stand, there was little to do but fasten parts together with bolts. Each piece must be exact as to size and must have the strength to bear its own load. The computations must be made with care if there is to be economy, as well as efficiency, in the construction.

For a discussion of the aesthetic value of form from the point of view of a mathe-matician, the reader is referred to the writ-

Mathematics in art

ings of Professor George D. Birkhoff which are listed in the Bibliography. The discussion takes into consideration the qualities of complexity, vertical symmetry, equilibrium, rotational symmetry, and close relation to a horizontal-vertical network, all of which have a pleasing aesthetic value, and other factors which have an unsatisfactory aesthetic measure, e.g., too small distances from vertices to vertices or sides, angles too near 0° or 180°, diversity of niches, unsupported re-entrant sides, diversity of directions, and lack of symmetry.

BIBLIOGRAPHY

E. T. Bell, *The Search for Truth.* New York: Reynal & Hitchcock, 1934.

G. D. Birkhoff, *Aesthetic Measure.* Cambridge: Harvard University Press, 1933.

G. A. Bliss, "Contributions That Have Been Made by Pure Science to the Advancement of Engineering and Industry," *Scientific Monthly,* XXIV (1927), 472.

T. C. Chamberlin, *Fundamental Problems of Geology.* Year Book No. 3 of the Carnegie Institution of Washington. Washington, 1905.

W. F. Durand (editor in chief), *Aerodynamic Theory.* 2 vols. Berlin: Julius Springer, 1934, 1935.

A. S. Eddington, *New Pathways in Science.* New York: Macmillan, 1935.

C. C. Furnas, *The Next Hundred Years.* Baltimore: Williams & Wilkins Co., 1935.

H. Glauert, *The Elements of Aerofoil and Airscrew Theory.* Cambridge: University Press, 1930.

W. H. McAdams, *Heat Transmission.* New York: McGraw-Hill, 1933.

F. R. Moulton, "On the Evolution of the Solar System," *Astrophysical Journal,* Vol. XXII, No. 3 (October, 1905).

F. R. Moulton, *New Methods in Exterior Ballistics.* Chicago: University of Chicago Press, 1926.

R. Rothe, F. Ollendorff, and K. Pohlhauser, *Theory of Functions as Applied to Engineering Problems.* Cambridge: Massachusetts Institute of Technology Press, 1933.

H. Schultz, "Interrelations of Demand, Income, and Price," *Journal of Political Economy,* XLIII, No. 4 (1935), 433.

T. Theodorsen and I. E. Garrick, *General Potential Theory of Arbitrary Wing Sections.* National Advisory Committee for Aeronautics, Report No. 452 (1933).

L. C. Thurstone, *The Vectors of Mind.* Chicago: University of Chicago Press, 1935.

JOURNALS

Annals of Mathematical Statistics
Econometrica
Journal of the American Statistical Association
Journal of Educational Psychology
Journal of Educational Research
Science
Scientific Monthly

ALGEBRAIC MANIPULATION

THESE pages are inserted to assist readers who have lived through several years since solving any algebraic problems and who have a feeling of uncertainty as to the method of performing the simplest algebraic manipulation. With no proofs or explanations we are merely showing the solutions of many types of problems and illustrating the use of technical terms.

1. Terminology. The algebraic expression x^2+3x-7 has three **terms** and is called a **trinomial** and also a **polynomial**; the expression $4ab-p^2$ has two terms and is called a **binomial**; while $13xyz$ has only one term and is a **monomial**. In the trinomial above, the **coefficient** of x^2 is 1, the coefficient of x is 3, and -7 is called the **constant term**.

2. Addition and subtraction.

$$a) \quad 2x+4-3y+5x+7y-1 = 7x+4y+3\ ,$$

$$b) \quad 4\sqrt{3}-\tfrac{1}{2}\sqrt{3}=\tfrac{7}{2}\sqrt{3}\ ,$$

$$c) \quad 2\sqrt{3}+5\sqrt{7}=2\sqrt{3}+5\sqrt{7}\ ,$$

$$d) \quad \begin{array}{cc} 4-3x & 4-3x \\ +(2+5x) & -(2+5x) \\ \hline 6+2x & 2-8x \end{array}\ .$$

3. Multiplication and division.

$$a) \quad 5a\times2b=10ab\ , \qquad b) \quad 5a\times(-2b)=-10ab\ ,$$

$$c) \quad (-5a)\times2b=-10ab\ , \qquad d) \quad (-5a)\times(-2b)=10ab\ ,$$

$$e) \quad 48\sqrt{5}\div4\sqrt{5}=12\ , \qquad f) \quad 6\sqrt{2}\times3\sqrt{3}=18\sqrt{6}\ .$$

In algebra there are many ways of indicating the *operation of division.* For example, division of 20 by 4 is written

$$20 \div 4 = 5 , \qquad 20/4 = 5 , \qquad \tfrac{20}{4} = 5, \qquad 20 \times \tfrac{1}{4} = 5 .$$

The quotient of 1 by a number N (viz., $1/N$) is called the **reciprocal** of N.

4. Equations. Proportion.

a) The symbol $a:b::c:d$ is called a **proportion.** The **terms** b and c are the **means,** and the terms a and d are the **extremes.** The term d is said to be the **fourth proportional** to a, b, and c. A proportion, however, *is an equation;* and when it is written in the form of an equation,

$$\frac{a}{b} = \frac{c}{d} ,$$

it is easy to find the value of any one of the four number-symbols when the remaining three are given. For example, we write,

$$a = \frac{bc}{d} , \qquad b = \frac{ad}{c} , \qquad c = \frac{ad}{b} , \qquad d = \frac{bc}{a} .$$

Proportions arise frequently in geometry in comparing similar triangles. We say, "Corresponding sides of similar triangles are proportional," and mean by this statement that if a and b are two sides of one of the triangles and c and d are the corresponding sides of the other triangle, we can write out the proportion $a:b::c:d$ or its equivalent, the equation $a/b = c/d$.

b) From $s = \tfrac{1}{2}at^2$ we get $2s = at^2$, $t^2 = \dfrac{2s}{a}$, and finally, $t = \sqrt{\dfrac{2s}{a}}$.

c) From $F = ma$ we can write $m = F/a$, and also $a = F/m$.

d) In the equation $v = at$, when t is doubled, v is doubled; when t is halved, v is halved, etc. The equation $c = 2\pi r$ shows that when the radius of the circle is trebled, the same is true of the circumference. This property is expressed by the statements:

    i) Velocity is *proportional* to the time,
    ii) The circumference of a circle is *proportional* to the radius.

We also say that velocity *varies as* the time and the circumference varies as the radius. These are **direct proportions.** When the relationship between two variables is like that between pressure and volume of a gas whose temperature remains constant, viz., $pv = $ const., or

$$p = \frac{c}{v},$$

it is an **indirect proportion,** since now doubling the volume halves the pressure and trebling the volume causes the pressure to become one-third of its original value.

That the statement "Velocity is proportional to time" is not always true is shown by the equation $v = v_0 + at$. When the time is doubled, the same is not true of the velocity. This is due to the fact that the velocity had a value v_0 (not zero) when t was zero. For both of the velocity equations we may say: "The *increase* in the velocity is proportional to the *increase* in the time."

5. Fractions.

$$a) \ \frac{1}{2} + \frac{1}{3} = \frac{2+3}{6} = \frac{5}{6}, \qquad c) \ \frac{1}{a} - \frac{1}{b} = \frac{b-a}{ab},$$

$$b) \ \frac{1}{a} + \frac{1}{b} = \frac{b+a}{ab}, \qquad d) \ \frac{a}{b} \times \frac{c}{d} = \frac{ac}{bd},$$

$$e) \ \frac{a}{b} \div \frac{c}{d} = \frac{ad}{bc}.$$

LAWS OF SINES, COSINES, AND EXPONENTS

I N THE solution of vector triangles on pages 73 and following, the Law of Sines and the Law of Cosines were used without proof. The proofs are now given.

The Law of Sines. The Law of Cosines. Let the angles of the triangle be denoted by A, B, C, and the opposite sides by a, b, c, respectively. Two

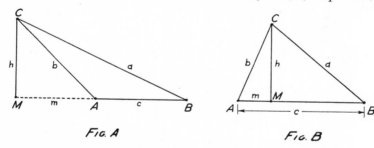

FIG. A   FIG. B

figures will be drawn. In the one, the oblique triangle has an obtuse angle. In the other, all of the angles are acute. In Figures A and B drop a perpendicular from the vertex at C to the side AB (produced if necessary), meeting AB at M. Let $AM = m$. We can now prove two laws:

LAW OF SINES

In Figure A

$h = a \sin B$,
$h = b \sin (180^0 - A) = b \sin A$.
$\therefore a \sin B = b \sin A$,
and, finally,

$$\frac{a}{b} = \frac{\sin A}{\sin B}.$$

In Figure B

$h = a \sin B$,
$h = b \sin A$.
$\therefore a \sin B = b \sin A$,

$$\frac{a}{b} = \frac{\sin A}{\sin B}.$$

LAW OF COSINES

In Figure A

$h^2 = a^2 - (c+m)^2$,

$h^2 = b^2 - m^2$,

$a^2 - (c+m)^2 = b^2 - m^2$,

$a^2 = b^2 + c + 2cm$,

$m = b \cos (180 - A) = -b \cos A$.

Hence

$a^2 = b^2 + c^2 - 2bc \cos A$.

In Figure B

$h^2 = a^2 - (c-m)^2$,

$h^2 = b^2 - m^2$,

$a^2 - (c-m)^2 = b^2 - m^2$,

$a^2 = b^2 + c^2 - 2cm$,

$m = b \cos A$.

Hence

$a^2 = b^2 + c^2 - 2bc \cos A$.

Let the lettering on the angles and sides of the triangle be changed as shown in Figures C and D. By repeating the preceding steps, we get

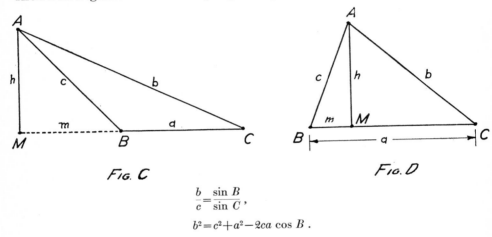

Fig. C   Fig. D

$$\frac{b}{c} = \frac{\sin B}{\sin C} ,$$

$$b^2 = c^2 + a^2 - 2ca \cos B .$$

Once more let us reletter the figures by replacing A by B, B by C, and C by A. This gives

$$\frac{c}{a} = \frac{\sin C}{\sin A} ,$$

$$c^2 = a^2 + b^2 - 2ab \cos C .$$

The three forms in which the sines of the angles appear constitute **the Law of Sines.** It may be written as a continued proportion, viz.,

$$a:b:c::\sin A:\sin B:\sin C.$$

In words it may be stated: *The ratio of any two sides of a triangle is equal to the ratio of the sines of their opposite angles.*

The three forms in which the cosines of the angle appear constitute the **Law of Cosines.** In words it may be stated: *The square on any side of a* *triangle is equal to the sum of the squares of the remaining two sides dimin-ished by twice the product of these two sides by the cosine of their included angle.*

Another way of writing the Law of Cosines is as follows:

$$\cos A = \frac{b^2 + c^2 - a^2}{2\ bc},$$

$$\cos B = \frac{c^2 + a^2 - b^2}{2\ ca},$$

$$\cos C = \frac{a^2 + b^2 - c^2}{2\ ab}.$$

EXPONENTS

1. Positive integer exponents. The product of the number 5 by itself is indicated by 5^2; the product $3 \times 3 \times 3 \times 3$ is indicated by 3^4; the symbol a^5 is a convenient notation for the product of five equal factors, i.e.,

$$a^5 = a \times a \times a \times a \times a.$$

Similarly, if n stands for a positive integer, the symbol b^n represents the number obtained by using b as a factor n times,

$$b^n = b \times b \times \ldots \times b \ (n \text{ factors}).$$

In this symbol, b is called the **base,** n the **exponent,** and b^n is the nth power of the base b.

With this agreement about the meaning of a positive integer expo-nent, it is easy to multiply, divide, raise to powers, and extract roots of numbers which are written as *powers of the same base.* In the left-hand column below are given some numerical examples which can be easily verified by replacing each symbol by the appropriate product of equal factors; in the right-hand column are exhibited general formulas. Follow-ing the examples and formulas, the laws are stated in words.* Each of these laws tells no more and no less than the general formula which has the same serial number.

---

* For a more complete discussion and proofs, see Logsdon, *Elementary Mathematical Analysis,* Vol. I, chap. v.

Examples   *Formulas*

1) $5^2 \times 5^2 = 5^4$,   1) $a^m \times a^n = a^{m+n}$,

2) $7^7 \div 7^4 = 7^3$,   2) $b^m \div b^n = b^{m-n}$, $(m > n)$,

3) $(3^2)^3 = 3^6$,   3) $(c^r)^p = c^{rp}$,

4) $\sqrt{2^{10}} = 2^2$.   4) $\sqrt[q]{d^p} = d^{p/q}$.

Laws of exponents for positive integers.

1. The exponent of the product of two powers of the same base is the sum of their exponents.

2. The exponent of the quotient of two powers of the same base is the exponent of the dividend minus the exponent of the divisor.

3. The exponent of the pth power of a power of a given base is p *times the given exponent of the base.*

4. The exponent of the qth root of a power of a given base is obtained by dividing the given exponent of the base by q.

2. Exponents which are not positive integers. If zero or a negative number or a fraction is to be used as an exponent, we can no longer say that the exponent indicates how many times the base is to be used as a factor. For convenience we agree to define symbols like a^0, a^{-2}, and $a^{\frac{1}{3}}$ in such a way that they will obey the laws obeyed by positive integer exponents. If, for example, the multiplication law is to hold, we shall have

$$\text{i)} \quad a^0 \cdot a^m = a^{0+m} = a^m ,$$

$$\text{ii)} \quad b^5 \cdot b^{-2} = b^3 ,$$

$$\text{iii)} \quad a^{\frac{1}{3}} \cdot a^{\frac{1}{3}} \cdot a^{\frac{1}{3}} = a .$$

Let us compare the last three equations with the following three equations:

$$\text{j)} \quad 1 \cdot a^m = a^m ,$$

$$\text{jj)} \quad b^5 \div b^2 = b^5 \times \frac{1}{b^2} = b^3 ,$$

$$\text{jjj)} \quad \sqrt[3]{a} = b \text{ if } b \times b \times b = a .$$

We conclude: (1) if the multiplication law is to hold for a^0, then a^0 behaves exactly like the number 1, since, when you multiply a number a^m by it, you obtain the same number, a^m; (2) the result of multiplying a power of b by b^{-2} is the same as dividing it by b^2 (or multiplying it by $1/b^2$);

(3) $a^{\frac{1}{3}}$ is the cube root of a, since, when you multiply together three like factors $a^{\frac{1}{3}}$ you get a.

In accord with these observations occasioned by use of the multiplication law, we shall make the following definitions:

$$\textit{Definition 1. } a^0 = 1.$$

$$\textit{Definition 2. } a^{-k} = \frac{1}{a^k}.$$

$$\textit{Definition 3. } a^{\frac{1}{q}} = +\sqrt[q]{a}.$$

With this agreement, we can easily satisfy ourselves that zero, negative, and fractional exponents also obey the other three laws of exponents for positive integers.

Physicists and astronomers deal with very large numbers, and physicists and chemists deal with very small numbers. Remembering that $10^0 = 1$, $10^1 = 10$, $10^2 = 100$, $10^3 = 1,000$, etc., and that $10^{-1} = 0.1$, $10^{-2} = 0.01$, $10^{-3} = 0.001$, etc., we can see how much simpler it is to write 2.47×10^{12} and 2.47×10^{-15} than to write out, without using exponents, the numbers which are equal to these.

APPENDIX C

ANSWERS—EXAMPLES—EXERCISES

CHAPTER 2, PAGE 20

I. (a) 7,923; (b) 62,285; (c) 3,862; (d) 32,147; (e) 67,366; (f) 3,211; (g) 1,976,949; (h) 219,600; (i) 21,630; (j) $2\frac{1}{4}$; (k) 14; (l) $23\frac{2}{9}$.

II.

Decimal	Binary	Ternary
a) 12	1,100	110
b) 20	10,100	202
c) 60	111,100	2,020
d) 42.5	101,010.1	1,120.111 . . . .
e) 0.06	0.00001111	0.00112 . . . .

III.

Decimal	Duodecimal	Vigesimal	Sexagesimal
a) 1,000	6φ4	2a0	. . .
b) 23,075	1,142φ	. . . . .	. . .
c) 948	670	278	. . .
d) 3,600	2,100	900	100
e) 42.5	36.6	22.a	. . .

When entries are not made, it is to give you the privilege of coining your own new number symbols.

CHAPTER 2, PAGE 27

EXAMPLES.

a) The sum of $4+3\sqrt{-5}$ and $6-7\sqrt{-5}$ is $10-4\sqrt{-5}$.

b) The sum of $2-4\sqrt{-7}$ and $3+5\sqrt{-6}$ is $5-4\sqrt{-7}+5\sqrt{-6}$.

c) The product of $2\sqrt{-5}$ and $6\sqrt{-5}$ is $12(-5)=-60$.

d) Subtract $4\sqrt{-8}$ from $12+3\sqrt{-8}$. The answer is $12-\sqrt{-8}=12-2\sqrt{-2}$.

e) Reduce the following numbers to the product of a real number by the square root of -1: (1) $\sqrt{-144}$, (2) $3\sqrt{-243}$, (3) $7\sqrt{-32}$.

f) Find the sum of $18+\sqrt{-144}$ and $7-\sqrt{-256}$.

g) Find the sum of $-5\sqrt{-28}$ and $9+\sqrt{-63}$.

h) Subtract $13+2\sqrt{-11}$ from $17+\sqrt{-99}$.

i) Subtract $8-5\sqrt{-6}$ from $13+\sqrt{-24}$.

j) Subtract $-23+\sqrt{-28}$ from $-1+2\sqrt{-7}$.

k) What values of x satisfy $x^2+256=0$?

l) What values of x satisfy $x^2+28=0$?

ANSWERS. (*e*) $12\sqrt{-1}$, $27\sqrt{3}\sqrt{-1}$, $28\sqrt{2}\sqrt{-1}$.   (*f*) $25-4\sqrt{-1}$.   (*g*) $9-7\sqrt{-7}$. (*h*) $4+\sqrt{-11}$. (*i*) $5+7\sqrt{-6}$. (*j*) 22. (*k*) $+16\sqrt{-1}$ and $-16\sqrt{-1}$. (*l*) $+2\sqrt{-7}$ and $-2\sqrt{-7}$.

CHAPTER 3, PAGE 53

(1) There are eight solutions to the problem of the lambs and calves. They are: (calves, lambs) $= (1, 35)$, $(3, 30)$, $(5, 25)$, $(7, 20)$, $(9, 15)$, $(11, 10)$, $(13, 5)$, $(15, 0)$.

(2) There are many solutions of the bond-investment problem. Two solutions are given here: He may buy (*i*) three $100 bonds at 45, (*ii*) three $100 bonds at 70, (*iii*) eleven $1,000 bonds at 105, and (*iv*) one $100 bond at 105. Or he may buy (*i*) two $1,000 bonds and four $100 bonds at 45, (*ii*) five $1,000 bonds and one $100 bond at 70, and (*iii*) seven $1,000 bonds at 105.

Another problem whose solution must be given in positive integers is this: Thirty-five cars are to be distributed in three different types of trucks which hold 3, 5, and 7 cars, respectively. How many trucks of each type will be able to transport all of the cars? One solution is (1, 5, 1).

CHAPTER 3, PAGE 59

A property may be bought for $4,000 cash or in annual instalments of $1,500 each, payable 1, 2, and 3 yr. after date. What is the annual interest rate which this offer implies?

By a formula in arithmetic, if r is the annual rate of interest, the $4,000 cash payment should be worth $4,000(1+r)^3$ at the end of 3 yr., while the instalment payments would be worth, at the end of 3 yr.,

$$1,500(1+r)^2+1,500(1+r)+1,500 .$$

These two numbers should be approximately equal; i.e., we seek the value of r which satisfies the equation

$$4,000(1+r)^3=1,500(1+r)^2+1,500(1+r)+1,500 .$$

The answer is approximately 6.1 per cent.

EXAMPLE. Find approximately the cube root of 5.

SOLUTION. We wish to find the real value of x which satisfies the equation $x^3=5$. We see that the value sought lies between 1 and 2. Let it be denoted by $1+h$. Then we set $x=1+h$ in the given equation and get

$$(1+h)^3-5=0 ,$$
$$h^3+3h^2+3h-4=0 .$$

This equation has a root between 0 and 1. By trial we find that when $h=0.7$, $h^3+3h^2+3h-4=-0.087$, and that when $h=0.8$, $h^3+3h^2+3h-4=+0.834$. Hence the value of h lies between 0.7 and 0.8., while the value of x lies between 1.7 and 1.8. Set $h = p+0.7$; then the value of p is less than 0.1 and it must satisfy the equation

$$(p+0.07)^3 + 3(p+0.07)^2 + 3(p+0.07) - 4 = 0 .$$

The process may be continued as far as desired. The answer, correct to five decimals, is 1.70998.

CHAPTER 5, PAGE 90

(Rectangular Cartesian coordinates are used in the following examples.)

1. Construct the graph $y = x+1$ by finding two solutions of the equation, plotting the points represented by the solutions and drawing a straight line through them. (Note: This method is valid because of the remark on page 90 that the graph of any linear equation is a straight line.)

2. Make the graph of each of these: $y = -x$, $y = -x+1$, $y = -x-1$. It can be proved that these graphs are parallel lines.

3. Draw the graph of $y = 2x$, $y = -\frac{1}{2}x$. It can be proved that these graphs are perpendicular lines.

4. Show that if a man goes from the point (0, 1) to the point (8, 1) he has gone 8 units. (These units may represent miles, or feet, etc.)

5. What is the area of each of the following rectangles?

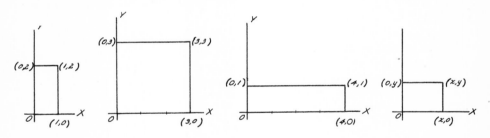

6. Show that the x-axis is not the complete graph of $xy = 0$ because criterion (1) on page 87 is not satisfied, although (2) is. Show that the x-axis and the y-axis together give the complete graph. (Note to student: The graph of an equation is usually a single line or curve; $xy = 0$ is an exception.)

7. Draw and interpret the graph of $y = 4x$ if y is the distance, in miles, of a man from a certain point P on a straight road, and x is the number of hours since the man was at P. If the equation $y = 4x$ accurately represents the man's position at all times, what is his speed?

CHAPTER 5, PAGE 93

1. If A is the point (1, 2), $B = (4, 4)$, $C = (-2, 0)$, show that the distances AB and AC are equal.

2. If $A = (-9, 0)$, $B = (0, 12)$, and $C = (16, 0)$, show that ABC is a right triangle by showing that $\overline{AC}^2 = \overline{AB}^2 + \overline{BC}^2$.

3. What is the terminal point of a vector which starts at the origin and which is equal to the vector $\overline{AB}$ of the figure? The vector $\overline{CD}$?

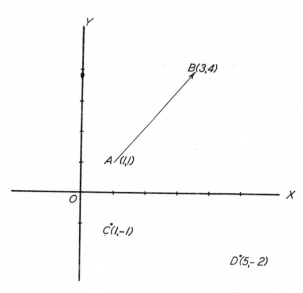

4. What is the length of the vector $\overline{AB}+\overline{CD}$?

5. Show that the point $(\sqrt{3}, 1)$ is on the circle $x^2+y^2=4$ by:

a) showing that its coordinates satisfy the equation, and also

b) showing that its distance from the origin is 2. Do the same for the points $(-\sqrt{3}, 1)$, $(\sqrt{3}, -1)$, $(1, \sqrt{3})$, $(-1, -\sqrt{3})$.

6. Show that the circle $(x-3)^2+(y+4)^2=25$ passes through the origin:

a) by showing that $x=0$, $y=0$ satisfy the equation.

b) by showing that the distance from the origin to the center of the circle is equal to the radius of the circle.

Plot the given circle.

7. Write the equations of the following circles:

a) center at $(4, -4)$; radius 10.

b) center at $(0, 0)$, radius 3.

c) center at $(0, 1)$, radius 4.

8. The equation $(x-h)^2+y^2=4$ represents an infinite number of circles, one for each value that can be assigned to h. What property do all these circles have in common? *Answer:* Their centers are on the x-axis; the radius of each is 2.

9. Draw the graph of the line $y=2x$, and the circle $(x-5)^2+(y+1)^2=25$ on the same figure. Show that they both go through the point $(1, 2)$.

CHAPTER 5, PAGE 95

Coordinates of center and radius.

(a) $(0, 3); 2$.   (b) $(2, 0); 2$.   (c) $(2, 3); 2$.   (d) $(-2, 3); 2$.
(e) $(2, -3); 2$.   (f) $(-2, -3); 2$.   (g) $(0, 0); \sqrt{2}$.

(1) All but (g) have radius 2.

(2) The center of circle (c) is in quadrant *I;* the center of (d) is in quadrant *II*, of (f) is in quadrant *III*, of (e) is in quadrant *IV;* the center of (b) is on the x-axis, and the center of (a) is on the y-axis.

(3) $4; 6, 2\sqrt{13}$.

(4) $(x-5)^2+y^2=4$; $(x-2)^2+(y-3)^2=4$; $(x-2)^2+(y+3)^2=4$.

(5) The equation is $(x-20)^2+(y-10)^2=900$; the distance of the tree from the fence corner is $10\sqrt{5}$ ft.; the equation of the east-west line through the tree is $y=10$; of the north-south line through the tree is $x=20$.

INDEX